SPANISH for the School Nurse's Office

by
Barbara Thuro

Published by Ammie Enterprises, Fallbrook, California

SPANISH FOR THE SCHOOL NURSE'S OFFICE

Ammie Enterprises
P.O. Box 151
Fallbrook, CA 92088-0151

fax (760) 451-2096

Printed in the United States of America

Library of Congress Card Catalog Number 85-070256

ISBN 0932825028

Introduction

This book was prepared to assist the professionally trained school nurse and other school personnel in providing assistance to students with medical problems needing to be addressed in the school setting. Hopefully, this book will help bridge the communication gap, making it possible for children who are ill or in pain to receive assistance more quickly. It is also the intent of this book to help improve communication between the school and the parent in regard to the health and safety of students. This book is not intended to take the place of professional medical advice.

Users need to be aware that Spanish medical terminology varies from one geographical area to another. It is advisable to verify the particular local usage.

Through use of the vocabulary lists, sentence patterns can be easily changed to construct sentences appropriate for specific situations.

Acknowledgements

I wish to thank the following whose hard work and professionalism made this book possible: Wanda Crews and Lois Powell, school nurses and consultants on the content of the book; Dr. Eleanor Meyer, Professor of Spanish at Long Beach City College, who served as Spanish language advisor; Shirley Thayer of Thayer Communications, for editorial assistance; and the staffs of both the Escondido Union School District and the Vista Unified School District for their cooperation throughout the development of the manuscript.

PRONUNCIATION GUIDE

Spanish Vowels	English Pronunciation
a	"ah" as in father
e (when ending a syllable)	"eh" as in let
e (when a syllable ends in a consonant)	"ay" as in say
i	"ee" as in see
o	"oh" as in open
u	"oo" as in moon

u is silent when preceeded by q (que = keh)

Spanish Consonants	English Pronunciation
c (followed by a, o, u)	"k" as in come
c (followed by e, i)	"s" as in this
g (followed by a, o, u)	"g" as in get
g (followed by e, i)	"h" as in hot
h	silent
j	"h" as in has
ll (like English y)	"y" as in yet
ñ	"ny" as in canyon
qu (followed by e, i)	"k" as in king
rr	trilled
v	"b" as in boy
z	"s" as in sun
y (is the Spanish word for "and")	"ee" as in see

Spanish Accents

Most words ending in a consonant, except n or s, are stressed on the last syllable, (example: juven**tud**, profe**sor**).

Most words ending in a vowel or n or s have the stress on the next to the last syllable, (example: **cla**se, **te**la, panta**lo**nes.

Words not pronounced according to these rules will have an accent mark on the syllable to be stressed, (example: lecci**ón**, tri**án**gulo).

TABLE OF CONTENTS

HEARING

COMMUNICABLE DISEASES

DENTAL HEALTH

NUTRITION

SUBSTANCE ABUSE

CHILD ABUSE

COMMUNICATING WITH PARENTS

TERMINOLOGY LISTS

Greeting the Student: Preliminary Conversation

1. Please wait here.
   Espera aquí, por favor.
2. Please wait a minute.
   Espera un momento, por favor.
3. You are next.
   Tú sigues.
4. It's your turn.
   Te toca a ti.
5. What is your name?
   ¿Cómo te llamas?
6. Come with me.
   Ven conmigo.
7. Come here.
   Ven aquí.
8. Sit down.
   Siéntate.
9. Please sit here.
   Siéntate aquí, por favor.
10. Please lie down here.
    Acuéstate aquí, por favor.

11. Lie down on the bed (cot) until I can help you.
    Acuéstate en la cama (camilla) hasta que pueda atenderte.

12. Just rest.
    Simplemente descansa.

13. Please stand up and come over here.
    Por favor, levántate y ven aquí.

14. Look at me.
    Mírame.

15. May I help you?
    ¿En qué puedo ayudarte?

16. How are you?
    ¿Cómo estás?

17. What do you want?
    ¿Qué quieres? o **¿Qué deseas?**

18. What grade (period, class) are you in?
    ¿En qué año (período, clase) estás?

19. Did you just come from the classroom (cafeteria, playground)?
    ¿Acabas de llegar de la clase (cafetería, patio de recreo)?

20. Who is your teacher?
    ¿Quién es tu maestro(a)?

21. Does your teacher know you are here?
    ¿Sabe tu maestro(a) que estás aquí?

22. Please speak more slowly.
    Habla más despacio, por favor.

23. Speak slowly and clearly.
    Habla despacio y claramente.

24. Do you have a teacher (an aide) who speaks Spanish?
    ¿Tienes un(a) maestro(a) (ayudante) que habla español?

25. Can you tell me in English?
    ¿Puedes decírmelo en inglés?

26. How old are you? When is your birthday?
    ¿Cuántos años tienes? ¿Cuál es la fecha de tu cumpleaños?

27. What school were you in last year?
    ¿En qué escuela estabas el año pasado?

28. Did you come from Mexico (Cuba, Puerto Rico)?
    ¿Viniste de México (Cuba, Puerto Rico)?

Examining, Questioning and Assisting a Student

General and Diagnostic Questions

1. What happened?
   ¿Qué pasó?

2. What's wrong?
   ¿Qué tienes? ¿Qué pasó?

3. Tell me what happened.
   Dime qué pasó.

4. How do you feel?
   ¿Cómo te sientes?

5. Tell me again.
   Dime otra vez. Repítemelo.

6. I don't understand.
   No entiendo.

7. Was there an accident?
   ¿Hubo un accidente?

8. Where (When) did it happen?
   ¿Dónde (Cuándo) pasó?

9. Were you in a fight?
   ¿Te peleaste?

10. Are you sick?
    ¿Estás enfermo(a)?

11. Don't you feel well?
    ¿No te sientes bien?

12. When did you begin to feel sick?
    ¿Cuándo empezaste a sentirte mal?

13. How long have you been sick?
    ¿Cuánto tiempo has estado enfermo(a)?

14. Were you sick yesterday (last night)?
    ¿Estabas enfermo(a) ayer (anoche)?

15. How did you feel yesterday (last night, this morning)?
    ¿Cómo te sentías ayer (anoche, esta mañana)?

16. Are you thirsty?
    ¿Tienes sed?

17. Are you nauseated?
¿Tienes náuseas?

18. Do you feel weak?
¿Te sientes débil?

19. Are you tired?
¿Estás cansado(a)?

20. Do you have a headache (stomachache)?
¿Tienes dolor de cabeza (dolor de estómago)?

21. Do you have any other kind of pain?
¿Tienes algún otro tipo de dolor?

22. Are you taking any kind of medicine?
¿Estás tomando algún tipo de medicina?

23. What are you taking?
¿Qué tomas?

24. Did a doctor prescribe the medicine?
¿Te recetó un médico la medicina?

25. Are you using any home remedies? What are they?
¿Usas algunos remedios caseros? ¿Qué son?

26. Did you eat your lunch?
¿Tomaste el almuerzo?

27. Did you eat breakfast today?
¿Tomaste el desayuno hoy?

28. What did you eat today for breakfast (lunch)?
¿Qué comiste hoy para el desayuno (almuerzo)?

29. When did you eat last?
¿Cuál fue tu última comida?

30. Why don't you want to eat?
¿Por qué no quieres comer?

31. Why aren't you hungry?
¿Por qué no tienes hambre?

32. Do you have any allergies?
¿Tienes alergias?

33. What time do you usually go to bed?
¿A qué hora te acuestas usualmente?

34. What time do you usually get up in the morning?
¿A qué hora te levantas usualmente por la mañana?

35. When did you last see a doctor?
¿Cuándo fue la última vez que fuiste a un médico?

36. What did you see him for?
¿Para qué lo viste?

37. Is this doctor still taking care of you?
¿Todavía te atiende ese doctor?

Injuries and Pain

1. Show me where it hurts.
Muéstrame dónde te duele.

2. Point to where you have the pain.
Indícame dónde te duele.

3. Take off your shoes and socks.
Quítate los zapatos y los calcetines.

4. Roll up your pant leg (sleeve).
Arremángate el pantalón (la manga).

5. If something hurts, tell me.
Si algo te duele, dímelo.

6. Don't touch it.
No lo toques.

7. Don't try to move it.
No trates de moverlo.

8. Bend over.
Dóblate.

9. Lean on me.
Apóyate en mí.

10. You have a (bad) cut.
Tienes una (mala) cortadura.

11. How did you get hurt?
¿Cómo te lastimaste?

12. What happened to your ______________? *
¿Qué le pasó a tu ____________________?

13. Did you fall?
¿Te caíste?

* Please refer to page 93 for "The Body and Bodily Functions."

14. How (Where) did you fall?
¿Cómo (Dónde) te caíste?

15. Can you walk?
¿Puedes caminar?

16. Don't try to move yourself.
No trates de moverte.

17. I'm going to put a splint (triangular bandage) on your arm (leg).
Te voy a poner una tablilla (venda triangular) en el brazo (la pierna).

18. Please hold it in place.
Por favor, sosténlo allí.

19. It will make you feel more comfortable until we can get you to a doctor.
Te hará sentirte más cómodo(a) hasta que te llevemos al médico.

20. Are you in pain now?
¿Tienes dolor ahora?

21. This will hurt a little.
Esto va a doler un poco.

22. You will be fine after you rest for a few minutes.
Estarás bien después de descansar unos minutos.

23. You will need to see a doctor.
Necesitas ver a un médico.

24. You will need to stay off the playground for the rest of the day.
No podrás jugar en el patio de recreo durante el resto del día.

25. I want to check your injury tomorrow.
Quiero examinar tu herida mañana.

26. If you hurt yourself again, let me know right away.
Si te lastimas otra vez, avísame inmediatamente.

Bee Stings

1. Did a bee sting you?
¿Te picó una abeja?

2. Have you ever been stung by a bee before?
¿Te ha picado una abeja antes?

3. What happened that time?
¿Qué pasó esa vez?

4. Did you have swelling or problems breathing?
¿Te hinchaste o tuviste problemas al respirar?

5. Did you see a doctor that time?
¿Viste a un médico esa vez?

6. What did the doctor say?
¿Qué te dijo el médico?

7. Do you know if you have an allergy to bee stings?
¿Sabes si tienes alergia a las picaduras de abeja?

8. I'm going to put this on your bee sting.
Voy a poner esto en la picadura.

9. Please sit here until I tell you that you can leave.
Por favor, siéntate aquí hasta que te diga que puedes salir.

10. We have the medicine the doctor prescribed for you for bee stings. I'm going to give it to you now.
Tenemos la medicina que el médico te recetó para las picaduras de abeja. Te la voy a dar ahora.

11. I'll need to call your parents and tell them you've been stung by a bee.
Necesito llamar a tus padres para decirles que te ha picado una abeja.

12. You will feel much better soon.
Pronto te sentirás mucho mejor.

Nose Bleeds

1. How did you get that bloody nose?
¿Cómo te empezó a sangrar la nariz?

2. Were you in a fight? Did you fall?
¿Te peleaste? ¿Te caíste?

3. I'm going to take care of it for you. Just do as I say.
Te voy a curar. Haz lo que te digo.

4. Lean slightly forward.
Inclínate un poco hacia delante.

5. Pinch your nostrils tight with the tissue for five minutes.
Apriétate la nariz con el pañuelo por cinco minutos.

6. Sit that way until I tell you to move.
Siéntate así hasta que te diga que te puedes mover.

7. Do not blow your nose for a few hours.
No te suenes la nariz por unas horas.

8. You can put the tissues in the wastebasket now and return to class.
Echa los pañuelos en la cesta ahora y vuelve a clase.

Bladder Control

1. Did you wet your pants?
   ¿Te mojaste los calzoncillos? ("calzones" for females)

2. We'll need to get you into some clean clothes.
   Tenemos que ponerte ropa limpia.

3. Do you have this problem very often?
   ¿Tienes este problema con frecuencia?

4. Do you wet the bed at night?
   ¿Mojas la cama por la noche?

5. I'll call your mother and have someone bring you a change of clothes.
   Llamaré a tu mama para que alguien te traiga ropa limpia.

Blisters

1. It looks like your blister broke.
   Parece que se abrió tu ampolla.

2. I'm going to wash it out with some soap and water.
   Voy a lavártela con agua y jabón.

3. I'll put a bandage on it.
   Te voy a poner una venda.

4. Maybe that will make it feel better.
   Quizás eso hará que te sientas mejor.

5. You'll have to stay off the bars for awhile.
   No podrás jugar en las barras por un tiempo.

6. You may return to class now.
   Puedes volver a clase ahora.

Sickness

Colds and Flu

1. Do you have a cold?
   ¿Tienes catarro?

2. Do you get a lot of colds?
   ¿Tienes muchos catarros? or **¿Te resfrías mucho?**

3. Do you cough frequently?
   ¿Toses con frecuencia?

4. Please cover your mouth when you cough.
   Cúbrete la boca cuando toses, por favor.

5. Please use your handkerchief.
   Usa el pañuelo, por favor.

6. Please blow your nose.
   Suénate la nariz, por favor.

7. Are you taking medicine for your cold (flu)?
   ¿Estás tomando medicina para el resfriado (la gripe)?

8. What have you taken?
   ¿Qué has tomado?

9. You should stay home when you are sick.
   Debes quedarte en casa cuando estás enfermo(a).

10. I want to examine your throat. Please open your mouth wide and say "ah."
    Quiero examinarte la garganta. Por favor, abre la boca bien y di "ah".

11. Your throat looks healthy.
    Tu garganta parece estar bien.

12. You have a very red, inflamed throat.
    Tienes la garganta muy inflamada y enrojecida.

13. You may have strep throat. You need to be examined by a doctor immediately.
    Es posible que tengas una infección (de estreptococo) de la garganta. Necesitas ser examinado(a) por un médico enseguida.

14. Lie down and I'll call your mother to come and pick you up.
    Acuéstate y llamaré a tu mamá para que venga a recogerte.

Fever

1. Open your mouth.
   Abre la boca.

2. Stick out your tongue.
   Saca la lengua.

3. I'm going to take your temperature.
   Voy a tomarte la temperatura.

4. Close your mouth.
   Cierra la boca.

5. Keep your mouth closed tight.
   Ten la boca cerrada.

6. You can open your mouth now.
   Puedes abrir la boca ahora.

7. I'll have to take your temperature under your arm.
   Tendré que tomarte la temperatura en el sobaco.

8. Please pull up your shirt (blouse).
   Por favor, levanta tu camisa (blusa).

9. Keep your arm tight to your body.
   Ten el brazo apretado contra el cuerpo.

10. I'm going to remove the thermometer now.
    Voy a quitarte el termómetro ahora.

11. You have (don't have) a fever.
    Tú tienes (no tienes) fiebre.

12. Do you know how long you have been running a fever?
    ¿Sabes desde cuándo tienes fiebre?

13. You should never come to school when you have a fever.
    Nunca debes venir a la escuela con fiebre.

14. You will have to go home now. I'll call your parents.
    Tendrás que irte a casa ahora. Llamaré a tus padres.

Nausea

1. Do you feel nauseated?
   ¿Estás mareado(a)? or **¿Tienes náusea?**

2. How long have you felt nauseated?
   ¿Desde cuándo estás mareado(a)? or **¿Desde cuándo tienes náusea?**

3. Do you have any idea what's causing your nausea?
   ¿Sabes lo que te causa tu náusea?

4. Have you been running around a lot on the playground?
   ¿Has corrido mucho en el patio de recreo?

5. Have you eaten something that made you sick?
   ¿Has comido algo que te puso enfermo(a)?

6. Have you vomited? More than once?
   ¿Has vomitado? ¿Más de una vez?

7. Did you vomit at home before you came to school?
   ¿Vomitaste en casa antes de venir a la escuela?

8. Lie down and rest awhile and see if you feel better.
   Acuéstate y descansa un rato a ver si te sientes mejor.

Checking for Contagious Diseases *

1. I need to check your head for lice. It will only take a minute.
   Te tengo que examinar la cabeza para ver si tienes piojos. Es sólo un momento.

2. You have head lice and will need to stay at home and use a special medicine until they are gone.
   Tienes piojos y necesitas quedarte en casa y usar una medicina especial hasta que desaparezcan.

3. You have ______________ and will need to go home and stay there until you are no longer contagious.
   Tienes ______________ y necesitas irte a casa y quedarte allí hasta que no estés contagioso(a).

4. You will need to see a doctor, and we will have to have a note from him before you return to school.
   Tendrás que ver a un médico, y necesitaremos una carta del médico antes de que regreses a la escuela.

* See page 31 for detailed information on contagious diseases.

Adolescent Concerns

Puberty

1. During puberty we begin to perspire more.
   Durante la pubertad empezamos a sudar más.

2. It is important to bathe daily and wear deodorant under the arms.
   Es importante bañarse diariamente y usar desodorante en las axilas (en los sobacos).

3. Our hair gets oilier, so we need to wash our hair more often.
   El pelo se pone más grasiento y por eso, es necesario lavarse el pelo más a menudo.

4. Due to the increase in oil and perspiration, we can get pimples (acne).
   A causa del aumento de grasa y sudor, podemos salir granos (acné).

5. The face should be washed with mild soap at least twice a day.
   Se debe lavar la cara con un jabón suave por lo menos dos veces al día.

6. Do not pinch the pimples.
   No te pellizques los granos.

7. This booklet on puberty will answer some of your questions.
   Este folleto acerca de la pubertad te contestará algunas de tus preguntas.

Scoliosis

1. I am going to test you for scoliosis (curvature of the spine).
   Te voy a examinar para ver si tienes escoliosis.

2. What is your name?
   ¿Cómo te llamas?

3. How old are you?
   ¿Cuántos años tienes?

4. Have you started your period yet?
   ¿Has comenzado a tener la regla?

5. Please remove your clothing from the waist up (except your bra).
   Por favor, quítate la ropa de la cintura para arriba (excepto el sostén).

6. Stand straight with your hands at your side and look at me.
   Estate derecho(a) con las manos a tus lados y mírame.

7. Let me look at your back.
   Déjame ver tu espalda.

8. Bend over with your hands together, like you are diving into a pool.
   Inclínate con las manos juntas, como si te zambulleras en una piscina.

9. Turn to the right (left), standing straight.
Dobla a la derecha (izquierda), manteniéndote derecho(a).

10. Now bend over.
Ahora inclínate hacia delante.

11. Turn toward me and bend over again.
Dobla hacia mí e inclínate hacia delante otra vez.

12. Thank you. You may get dressed now.
Gracias. Puedes vestirte ahora.

13. If further testing is necessary, we will notify you.
Si necesitas más exámenes, te avisaremos.

Menstruation

1. Monthly menstrual periods start sometime between the ages of nine and sixteen.
La menstruación (La regla) empieza entre la edad de nueve y dieciséis años.

2. When you are having a period it is important to change your pad or tampon every three or four hours.
Cuando tienes la regla es importante cambiar la servilleta higiénica o tampón cada tres o cuatro horas.

3. Wrap the pad (tampon) in toilet paper and put it in the container. Do not flush it down the toilet.
Envuelve la servilleta higiénica (tampón) en papel higiénico y ponla (ponlo) en el recipiente. No la (lo) pongas en el inodoro.

4. Sometimes when girls have their period they suffer from cramps. It may be necessary to take medication to relieve the pain.
A veces, cuando las muchachas tienen la regla, sienten calambres. Quizás sea necesario tomar medicina para aliviar el dolor.

5. A girl can become pregnant as soon as she has had her first period. Girls as young as eleven have become pregnant.
Una muchacha puede ponerse embarazada tan pronto como tenga la regla por primera vez. Las niñas de once años pueden ponerse embarazadas.

6. Here is a helpful book on menstruation. It will answer a lot of your questions.
Aquí tienes un libro útil acerca de la regla. Contestará muchas de tus preguntas.

Possible Pregnancy

1. When was your last period? Was it normal?
   ¿Cuándo tuviste la regla últimamente? ¿Fue normal?

2. Do you think you might be pregnant?
   ¿Crees que es posible que estés encinta (embarazada)?

3. Do you have any of the symptoms such as nausea or sore, swollen nipples?
   ¿Tienes algunos de los síntomas como náusea o pezones inflamados y doloridos?

4. Have you discussed this with your parents?
   ¿Has hablado de esto con tus padres?

5. You need to visit a doctor or clinic as soon as possible.
   Necesitas ir a un médico o una clínica lo más pronto posible.

Medical Treatment and Medicine

1. I'm going to give you your medicine.
   Voy a darte tu medicina.

2. Please fill the paper cup with water.
   Por favor, llena el vaso de papel con agua.

3. Take this pill (medicine).
   Toma esta píldora (medicina).

4. I'm going to wash (bandage) your cut.
   Te voy a lavar (poner una venda en) la cortadura.

5. I'm going to change your bandage.
   Voy a cambiarte la venda.

6. This may hurt a little.
   Puede que esto duela un poco.

7. I'm going to put an ice pack on your ________________. *
   Voy a ponerte una bolsa de hielo en tu ________________.

8. Please hold it on your injury.
   Por favor, mantenla apretada contra tu herida.

* Please refer to page 93 for "The Body and Bodily Functions."

Height and Weight

1. Take off your shoes.
   Quítate los zapatos.

2. Step on the scale.
   Ponte en la balanza.

3. I want to see how much you weigh.
   Quiero ver cuánto pesas.

4. Stand here (there).
   Estate aquí (allí).

5. I want to see how tall you are.
   Quiero ver tu estatura.

6. Put your feet flat on the scale and stand tall.
   Pon los pies planos en la balanza y estate derecho(a).

7. Thank you. You can put your shoes back on now.
   Gracias. Puedes ponerte los zapatos ahora.

Using the Bathroom and Cleaning Up

1. Do you have to go to the bathroom?
   ¿Tienes que ir al baño?

2. Do you know where the bathroom is? Let me show you.
   ¿Sabes dónde está el baño? Déjame mostrarte.

3. Can you show ________________ where the bathroom is? (spoken to another child)
   ¿Puedes mostrar a ________________ dónde está el baño?

4. The bathroom is next to the office (down the hall).
   El baño está al lado de la oficina (al fondo del pasillo).

5. Can you wait just a little while before you go?
   ¿Puedes esperar un poco más antes de ir?

6. I'm going to wash your ________________.
   Te voy a lavar la (el) ______________________.

7. Let me wipe that off for you.
   Déjame limpiarte eso.

8. Put your hand (finger, arm) in the sink and I'll rinse it off.
   Pon la mano (el dedo, el brazo) en el lavabo y te la (lo) enjuagaré.

9. Please wash your hands.
   Lávate las manos, por favor.

Sending a Student Home

1. I'm going to send you home.
   Te voy a mandar a casa.

2. You have to stay home until you are well.
   Tienes que quedarte en casa hasta que te sientas bien.

3. You have head lice and need to stay home for treatment until they are gone.
   Tienes piojos en la cabeza y necesitas quedarte en casa durante el tratamiento hasta que desaparezcan.

4. When you do return to school, come to the office to be checked before returning to class, to be sure the head lice are gone.
   Cuando regreses a la escuela, ven a la oficina para que te revisemos antes de que vayas a tu clase, para asegurarnos de que ya no tengas piojos.

5. You need to see a doctor.
   Necesitas ir a un médico.

6. I will make an appointment at the clinic (doctor) for you.
   Te voy a hacer una cita con la clínica (el médico) a ti.

7. Your mother needs to make an appointment at the clinic (with the doctor).
   Tu mamá necesita hacer una cita con la clínica (el médico).

8. You need to bring a note from the clinic (doctor).
   Necesitas traer una nota de la clínica (del médico).

9. Take this paper home and give it to your parents.
   Lleva este papel a casa y dáselo a tus padres.

10. Did you bring a coat to school?
    ¿Trajiste un abrigo a la escuela?

11. Do you have anything in your classroom that you need to take home?
    ¿Tienes algo en tu sala de clase que necesitas llevar contigo a casa?

12. Is your mother (anyone) at home?
    ¿Está en casa tu mamá (alguien)?

13. Does your mother work? Where?
    ¿Trabaja tu mamá? ¿Dónde?

14. Do you have a phone?
    ¿Tienes teléfono?

15. What is your phone number?
    ¿Cuál es tu número de teléfono?

16. Wait here while I call your mother.
Espera aquí mientras llamo a tu mamá.

17. Does your mother (babysitter) speak English?
¿Habla inglés tu mamá (la niñera)?

18. Who takes care of you if your mother is not at home?
¿Quién te cuida si tu mamá no está en casa?

19. Your mother is going to come for you.
Tu mamá te va a venir a recoger.

20. I want to see you the first day you return to school.
Quiero verte el primer día que regreses a la escuela.

21. I hope you feel better soon.
Espero que te sientas mejor pronto.

Reassuring a Student

1. Are you afraid?
¿Tienes miedo?

2. Don't be afraid.
No tengas miedo.

3. What are you afraid of?
¿De qué tienes miedo?

4. There is nothing in the nurse's office to be afraid of.
No hay nada de que tener miedo en la oficina de la enfermera.

5. This will not hurt you.
Esto no va a dolerte.

6. Are you afraid of something in class?
¿Tienes miedo de algo en la clase?

7. Are you afraid of someone here at school? Another student?
¿Tienes miedo de alguien en la escuela? ¿De otro(a) alumno(a)?

8. Are you afraid to read aloud?
¿Tienes miedo de leer en voz alta?

9. Are you afraid the teacher will call on you?
¿Tienes miedo de que el (la) maestro(a) te haga hablar?

10. Are you afraid you won't know the answer?
¿Tienes miedo de no saber la respuesta?

11. Do you feel you don't have friends?
¿Te parece que no tienes amigos?

12. Are you afraid to speak English?
Tienes miedo de hablar inglés?

13. Do you feel you don't know enough English?
¿Crees que no sabes bastante inglés?

14. I hear you are learning English very quickly.
He oído que estás aprendiendo el inglés muy rápidamente.

15. Are you afraid others will laugh at you? Why?
¿Tienes miedo de que los otros se rían de ti? ¿Por qué?

16. Can you draw me a picture about it or tell me in Spanish?
¿Me puedes hacer un dibujo acerca de eso o decírmelo en español?

17. I care and am interested in what you have to tell me.
Me importas y tengo interés en lo que me dices.

18. I like it when you tell me about yourself.
Me gusta cuando me hablas de ti.

19. Everything looks fine.
Todo parece estar bien.

20. Everything is going to turn out just fine.
Todo va a salir perfectamente bien.

21. You are very brave.
Eres muy valiente.

22. I'm so proud of you.
Estoy muy orgulloso(a) de ti.

23. Your parents will be proud of you.
Tus padres estarán orgullosos de ti.

24. Your teacher tells me you are doing well in class.
Tu maestro(a) me ha dicho que estás haciendo buen trabajo en la clase.

25. Your teacher tells me you are a very good worker.
Tu maestro(a) me ha dicho que eres un buen trabajador (una buena trabajadora).

26. You are a very good boy (girl).
Eres un buen niño (una buena niña).

27. I hope you feel better soon.
Ojalá que te sientas mejor pronto.

28. I know you will feel better very soon.
Yo sé que te sentirás mejor muy pronto.

Excusing a Student

1. Who is your teacher?
   ¿Quién es tu maestro(a)?

2. Take this to your teacher (counselor, vice principal).
   Lleva esto a tu maestro(a) [consejero(a), vice director(a)].

3. Can you go back to your room by yourself?
   ¿Puedes regresar a tu clase solo(a)?

4. Go right back to class.
   Ve directamente a clase.

5. I'll take you back to class.
   Yo te llevaré a tu clase.

6. When you are in class and need to use the rest room, raise your hand.
   Cuando estás en la clase y necesitas usar el baño, levanta la mano.

7. Your teacher tells me you need to be in school every day, if you are not sick.
   Tu maestro(a) me dice que tú debes estar en la escuela todos los días, si no estás enfermo(a).

8. Your teacher tells me you need to come to school on time.
   Tu maestro(a) me dice que tienes que venir a la escuela puntualmente.

9. Come with me to the office.
   Ven conmigo a la oficina.

10. Please be careful.
    Ten cuidado, por favor.

11. I hope you feel better soon.
    Espero que te sientas mejor pronto.

12. I want to see you again tomorrow (in one week).
    Quiero verte otra vez mañana (en una semana).

13. Please come before class or during recess.
    Por favor, ven antes de las clases o durante el recreo.

14. If you hurt yourself again, let me know right away.
    Si te lastimas otra vez, avísame inmediatamente.

15. Take care of yourself.
    Cuídate.

Vision and Hearing

Conversing with a Student

1. Let me look at your eye.
   Déjame verte el ojo.

2. Do you have something in your eye?
   ¿Tienes algo en el ojo?

3. Why is your eye red?
   ¿Por qué está rojo tu ojo?

4. Have you been rubbing your eye?
   ¿Te has estado refregando el ojo?

5. Please don't rub your eye.
   Por favor, no te refriegues el ojo.

6. I'm going to wash out your eye with water.
   Te voy a lavar el ojo con agua.

7. It won't hurt.
   No te va a doler.

8. Just lean over the sink.
   Inclínate hacia delante sobre el lavabo.

9. Keep your eyes closed for awhile.
   Manten los ojos cerrados por un rato.

10. Open your eyes now.
Abre los ojos ahora.

11. Do you have trouble with your eyes?
¿Tienes problemas con tus ojos?

12. Do your eyes bother you when you read?
¿Te duelen los ojos cuando lees?

13. Can you see what is written on the chalkboard in class?
¿Puedes ver lo que se escribe en la pizarra en clase?

14. Do you wear glasses?
¿Usas lentes (anteojos, gafas)?

15. Where are your glasses?
¿Dónde están tus lentes (anteojos, gafas)?

16. How did your glasses get broken?
¿Cómo se rompieron tus lentes (anteojos, gafas)?

17. Do you have another pair at home?
¿Tienes otros en casa?

18. Do you wear contact lenses?
¿Usas lentes de contacto?

19. When did you last see an eye doctor?
¿Cuándo fue la última vez que fuiste al oculista?

20. Did you get your glasses this year?
¿Te has comprado tus lentes este año?

21. What is your eye doctor's name?
¿Cuál es el nombre de tu oculista?

22. You need to see a doctor for a full eye exam.
Necesitas ir a un médico para un examen completo de tus ojos.

23. You have pinkeye (conjunctivitis) and need to see a doctor immediately.
Tienes conjuntivitis y necesitas ir a un médico en seguida.

24. You cannot return to school until you are no longer contagious.
No puedes regresar a la escuela hasta que no estés contagioso(a).

25. You need a prescription for eye medication from your doctor.
Necesitas obtener una receta de tu médico para medicina de los ojos.

26. Please take this note to your mother (parents).
Por favor lleva esta nota a tu mamá (tus padres).

27. You may return to class now.
Puedes regresar a tu clase ahora.

Vision Testing

1. This is a vision test.
   Este es un examen de la vista.

2. Please sit in this (that) chair.
   Por favor, siéntate en esta (esa) silla.

3. You may keep your glasses on to take the test.
   Puedes dejarte puestos los lentes durante el examen.

4. Hold this eye cover in front of your left (right) eye but keep both eyes open.
   Sostén esta cubierta delante del ojo izquierdo (derecho), pero manten ambos ojos abiertos.

5. Point your right (left) hand in the same direction as the black legs on the letter.
   Pon tu mano derecha (izquierda) en la misma dirección de las patas negras de las letras.

6. Read the letters of the alphabet that I point to.
   Lee las letras del abecedario que yo te indique.

7. You need to take your glasses off for the next part of the exam.
   Necesitas quitarte los lentes para la próxima parte del examen.

8. Thank you. You may return to class now.
   Gracias. Puedes regresar a clase ahora.

Communicating with Parents

1. Does your child have problems seeing?
   ¿Tiene su niño(a) problemas de la vista?

2. Does your child frequently have itchy eyes?
   ¿Tiene su niño(a) frecuentemente picazón en los ojos?

3. Do ______________'s eyelids often become red or swollen?
   Se le enrojecen o se le hinchan con frecuencia los párpados a __________ ?

4. Do his (her) eyes look bloodshot?
   ¿Tiene él (ella) los ojos enrojecidos?

5. Do they water?
   ¿Le lloran los ojos?

6. Do they burn or itch?
   ¿Le queman los ojos? ¿Le pican los ojos?

7. Do your child's eyes cross? When?
   ¿Se le tuerce la vista? ¿Cuándo?

8. Has your child ever had an eye operation?
¿Ha tenido su hijo(a) una operación en los ojos?

9. Does ______________ wear contact lenses?
¿Usa ______________ lentes de contacto?

10. Your child has pinkeye.
Su niño(a) tiene conjuntivitis.

11. Your child needs to be seen by a doctor for special medication.
Su hijo(a) debe ir a un médico para recibir medicina especial.

12. Please bring a note from the doctor when your child returns to school, advising us of the treatment.
Por favor traiga una nota del médico cuando su hijo(a) regrese a la escuela, informándonos sobre el tratamiento.

13. He (She) needs to stay at home until cured and is no longer contagious.
El (Ella) necesita quedarse en casa hasta que esté curado(a) y ya no esté contagioso(a).

14. Your child has been squinting while reading.
Su niño(a) ha estado bizqueando mientras lee.

15. The results of the school eye exam show that ________________ .
Los resultados de la prueba ocular de la escuela indican que ______________ .

16. Your child needs to see an eye doctor (optometrist, opthomologist) and bring us a note from the doctor after the exam.
Su hijo(a) necesita ver a un oculista (optometrista, oftalmólogo) y traernos una nota del médico después del examen.

17. Call or visit the clinic for an eye exam.
Llame o vaya a la clínica para un examen de los ojos.

18. The phone number is ______________.
El número de teléfono es ______________.

19. The address is ______________.
La dirección es ______________.

20. ____________broke his (her) glasses at school.
____________rompió sus lentes en la escuela.

21. __________ came to school again today without his (her) glasses. Are they lost (broken)?
__________vino a la escuela otra vez sin sus lentes. ¿Los ha perdido? ¿Están rotos?

22. ___________needs to bring his (her) glasses to school every day.
___________necesita traer sus lentes a la escuela todos los días.

23. Can you afford to buy glasses for ______________?
¿Puede usted costear el comprarle lentes a ______________?

Vision Terminology

blind	**ciego(a)**
color blind	**ciego(a) para los colores**
conjunctivitis	**la conjuntivitis**
contact lenses	**los lentes de contacto**
cornea	**la córnea**
corrective glasses	**los lentes correctivos**
cross-eyed	**bizco(a)**
deterioration of vision	**el deterioro de la vista**
eye(s)	**el (los) ojo(s)**
eyeball	**el globo del ojo**
eye doctor	**el oculista** **el oftalmólogo** **el optometrista**
eye examination	**el examen de la vista**
eyelash	**la pestaña**
eyelid	**el párpado**
eyesight	**la vista**
eye socket	**la cuenca del ojo**
eyestrain	**la vista fatigada**
eye test chart	**el cuadro gráfico para exámenes de la vista**
eyewash	**el colirio**
glasses	**los lentes** **los anteojos** **las gafas**
myopia	**la miopía**
nearsighted	**miope**
ophthalmologist	**el (la) oftalmólogo(a)**
optometrist	**el (la) optometrista**
see, to	**ver**
squint, to	**bizquear**

Name of Child: ______________________ School: ________________ Date: ________
Address: ______________________________ Telephone Number: ______________
Grade: __________ Track: _________ Teacher: __________________________

Dear Parents or Guardians:

Recently, we tested your child's eyesight at our school. Because of the test results, we believe your child should have a complete eye examination. We urge you to have this done as soon as possible. Please take this form to your eye examiner and ask him/her to complete it. Please return the completed form to the school as soon as possible. If you need more information, please contact our school nurse.

Note to Eye Examiner:

We have recommended that the parents seek out a complete examination because of:

Performance on Snellen Test: R. 20/ L. 20/ Both 20/
Signs and Symptoms:

____

The school looks forward to a report from you with any recommendations you desire to make. This information will help us plan the best educational program for this child.

- -

Report of Eye Examiner to the School

Name of Child: ____________________ School: ______________ Date: ______________

Visual Acuity

Distance Vision:

Without lenses
R. 20/ L. 20/
Both 20/

With lenses
R. 20/ L. 20/
Both 20/

Near Vision:

Without lenses
R. 20/ L. 20/
Both 20/

With lenses
R. 20/ L. 20/
Both 20/

Glasses

____ Not prescribed
____ Prescribed
____ To be worn all the time
____ To be worn for close work only
____ To be worn for distance only

Preferential seating recommended: ________________________________
Special materials that would be helpful: ____________________________
Other recommendations or suggestions: ____________________________
Date patient should return for further examination: ____________________

Signature: ______________________________ Date: ______________

Address: _______________________________ Telephone: ______________

Nombre del Niño(a): ____________________ Escuela: ________________ Fecha: ____________
Dirección: ____________________________________ Número de Teléfono: ________________
Grado: _______ Horario: _______ Maestro/a: ____

Estimados Padres o Tutores:

Como resultado de un reciente examen de la vista de su niño(a) en la escuela, creemos que su niño(a) debería de tener un completo examen de los ojos. Les rogamos que presten su pronta atención a esto. Por favor lleven este impreso a la persona que examine los ojos de su niño(a) y pídanle que lo complete. Favor de devolverlo a la escuela tan pronto como sea posible. Si desean más información, por favor comuníquense con la enfermera escolar.

Note to Eye Examiner:

We have recommended that the parents seek out a complete examination because of:

Performance on Snellen Test: R. 20/ L. 20/ Both 20/
Signs and Symptoms:

____

The school looks forward to a report from you with any recommendations you desire to make. This information will help us plan the best educational program for this child.

- -

Report of Eye Examiner to the School

Name of Child: ______________________ School: __________________ Date: __________

Visual Acuity

Distance Vision:

Without lenses
R. 20/ L. 20/
Both 20/

With lenses
R. 20/ L. 20/
Both 20/

Near Vision:

Without lenses
R. 20/ L. 20/
Both 20/

With lenses
R. 20/ L. 20/
Both 20/

Glasses

____ Not prescribed
____ Prescribed
____ To be worn all the time
____ To be worn for close work only
____ To be worn for distance only

Preferential seating recommended: ______________________________________
Special materials that would be helpful: ___________________________________
Other recommendations or suggestions: ___________________________________
Date patient should return for further examination: _________________________

Signature: ____ Date: ______________

Address: ____ Telephone: ___________

Hearing

Conversing with a Student

1. Can you hear me?
   ¿Puedes oírme?

2. Do you have a problem hearing?
   ¿Tienes dificultad en oír?

3. Do you have an earache?
   ¿Tienes dolor del oído?

4. How long has it hurt?
   ¿Por cuánto tiempo te ha dolido?

5. Have you been seen by a doctor for this problem?
   ¿Te ha examinado un médico por este problema?

6. Do you have earaches often?
   ¿Tienes frecuentes dolores del oído?

7. Is it hard for you to hear in class?
   ¿Te es difícil oír en clase?

8. Do you have something in your ear? Let me look.
   ¿Tienes algo en el oído? Déjame ver.

9. Have you ever had tubes in your ears?
   ¿Has tenido tubos en los oídos alguna vez?

10. How old were you when you had them?
    ¿Cuántos años tenías cuando los tuviste?

11. You may have an ear infection.
    Es posible que tengas una infección del oído.

12. You need to see a doctor for an ear exam.
    Necesitas ir a un médico para un examen del oído.

13. Be sure and let me know the results of the doctor's examination.
    No se te olvide informarme sobre los resultados del examen médico.

Hearing Testing

1. I'm going to give you a hearing test.
   Voy a darte un examen de tu capacidad de oír.

2. Don't be afraid. It's fun to listen.
   No tengas miedo. Te divertirás escuchando.

3. I'm going to put these earphones on you.
Te voy a poner estos audífonos.

4. Listen carefully.
Escucha atentamente.

5. Every time you hear a different sound, put your hand up on the same side where you hear the sound.
Cada vez que oigas un sonido diferente, levanta la mano del lado en el que oyes el sonido.

6. Put your hand down as soon as the sound goes away.
Baja la mano tan pronto como se acabe el sonido.

7. You are finished now. You did a good job.
Has terminado ahora. Lo has hecho muy bien.

8. You may return to class now.
Puedes regresar a clase ahora.

Communicating with Parents

1. Your child is having problems hearing at school.
Su hijo(a) tiene problemas con su capacidad de oír en la escuela.

2. Have you noticed a problem at home?
¿Ha (Han) notado que su hijo(a) tenga algún problema en casa?

3. Has your child ever had an ear operation?
¿Ha tenido su hijo(a) una operacion de los oídos?

4. Has your child ever had tubes in his (her) ears?
¿Ha tenido su niño(a) tubos en los oídos?

5. Does he (she) have trouble locating the source of sounds?
¿Tiene él (ella) dificultad de saber de dónde vienen los sonidos?

6. Your child needs to see a doctor for a more complete hearing evaluation.
Su niño(a) necesita ir a un doctor para una evaluación más completa de su capacidad de oír.

7. Your child appears to have an infection and needs to be seen by a doctor as soon as possible.
Su hijo(a) parece tener una infección y es importante que lo (la) examine un médico lo más pronto posible.

8. I will send you a report of my exam for you to take to the doctor.
Voy a mandarles un reporte de mi examen para que lo lleven a su médico.

Hearing Terminology

ear(s)	**el oído (los oídos)**
outer ear	**la oreja**
inner ear	**el oído interno**
earache	**el dolor de oído**
eardrum	**el tímpano**
earwax	**la cera de los oídos**
hearing (sense)	**la capacidad de oír**
hearing (hard of)	**duro de oído** **algo sordo**
hearing aid	**el aparato auditivo**
hearing loss	**la pérdida de la capacidad de oír**

Communicable Diseases

Mumps
Paperas

SYMPTOMS (Síntomas):

Fever, swelling and tenderness in front of and below the ear or under the jaw.
Fiebre, hinchazón y sensibilidad delante y debajo del oído o debajo de la quijada.

Painful to move jaws.
Es doloroso mover la quijada.

INCUBATION PERIOD (Período de Incubación):

Twelve to twenty-six days.
De doce a veintiséis días.

TREATMENT (Tratamiento):

Sick children are to be kept at home resting in bed until swelling of the glands and organs and all other symptoms have disappeared.
Los niños enfermos deben quedarse en casa, descansando en cama, hasta que la hinchazón de las glándulas y órganos y todos los otros síntomas hayan desaparecido.

Measles
Sarampión

SYMPTOMS (Síntomas):

Runny nose, coughing, watery eyes and fever. Blotchy rash about the fourth day.
Nariz mucosa, tos, ojos llorosos y fiebre. Sarpullido con manchas, aproximadamente al cuarto día.

INCUBATION PERIOD (Período de Incubación):

Eight to thirteen days.
De ocho a trece días.

TREATMENT (Tratamiento):

Sick children must remain at home a minimum of seven days from appearance of rash and drink plenty of fluids.
Los niños enfermos deben quedarse en casa por lo menos siete días desde que aparece el sarpullido, y deben beber mucho líquido.

German Measles
Rubéola, Sarampión Alemán

SYMPTOMS (Síntomas):

Light rash with mild fever. Glands behind ears and neck are enlarged.
Ligero sarpullido, con fiebre leve; las glándulas detrás de las orejas y en el cuello están hinchadas.

INCUBATION PERIOD (Período de Incubación):

Two to three weeks
De dos a tres semanas

TREATMENT (Tratamiento):

Sick children must remain at home for a minimum of four days from onset of rash until all symptoms have disappeared.
Los niños enfermos deben quedarse en casa por lo menos cuatro días desde que aparece el sarpullido, hasta que todos los síntomas hayan desaparecido.

Chicken Pox
Varicela, Viruela Loca

SYMPTOMS (Síntomas):

Small water blisters or pimples which dry into scabs appear on scalp and body.
Pequeñas ampollas o granos, que se secan formando costras, aparecen en la cabeza y partes del cuerpo.

The child may become irritable; tires easily.
El niño(a) puede ponerse de mal humor y cansarse fácilmente.

INCUBATION PERIOD (Período de Incubación):

Two to three weeks (usually 13 to 21 days)
De dos a tres semanas (generalmente de trece a veintiún días)

TREATMENT (Tratamiento):

Sick children must be kept at home for seven days from the appearance of the rash or until the blisters are dry and crusted.
Los niños enfermos deben quedarse en casa por siete días desde que aparece la erupción, o hasta que las ampollas estén secas y sean costras.

If the child has a fever a doctor should be consulted.
Si el niño tiene fiebre se debe consultar a un médico.

Whooping Cough (Pertussis)

Tos Ferina o Tos Convulsiva

SYMPTOMS (Síntomas):

Fever, a runny nose and persistent cough, which later comes in spells and ends in a whoop.
Fiebre, nariz mucosa y tos persistente, que después viene en intervalos y termina en un estertor.

Coughing may cause vomiting.
La tos puede causar vómito.

INCUBATION PERIOD (Período de Incubación):

Seven to ten days (up to twenty-one)
De siete a diez días (hasta veintiún días)

TREATMENT (Tratamiento):

Sick children should be confined to the home during the catarrhal and fever stages and for three weeks from the beginning of the severe coughing stage.
Los niños enfermos deben quedarse en casa durante la etapa de catarro y fiebre, y por tres semanas desde el comienzo de la etapa de tos severa.

Especially serious for infants. (Have babies immunized early.)
Especialmente peligroso para los bebés. (Se debe vacunar a los bebés lo más pronto posible.)

Scarlet Fever
Fiebre Escarlatina

SYMPTOMS (Síntomas):

Vomiting, fever, headache, sore throat, swollen glands in the neck. A bright rash usually appears in 24 hours.
Vómito, fiebre, dolor de cabeza, dolor de garganta, glándulas hinchadas en el cuello. Un sarpullido de color intenso usualmente aparece en veinte y cuatro horas.

INCUBATION PERIOD (Período de Incubación):

One to five days
De uno a cinco días

TREATMENT (Tratamiento):

The child should see a doctor for diagnosis and to start antibiotic therapy.
El niño debe ver a un médico para obtener el diagnóstico y para empezar la terapía con antibióticos.

Children are to be kept home until recovery and complete disappearance of symptoms.
Los niños(as) enfermos deben quedarse en casa hasta que se mejoren y hasta que todos los síntomas hayan desaparecido totalmente.

They are not contagious after two days of antibiotic therapy.
No están contagiosos después de dos días de tomar antibióticos.

Impetigo
El Impétigo

SYMPTOMS (Síntomas):

Infectious sores primarily on the face, nose and ears. It starts with small water blisters and becomes a sore that spreads. Sores are usually covered by a yellowish-brown crust which weeps thick fluid.

Erupción cutánea infecciosa principalmente en la cara, la nariz y las orejas. Empieza con unas pequeñas ampollas que se hacen úlceras que se extienden. Generalmente las úlceras se cubren con costras de color amarillento-marrón que supuran un líquido espeso.

TREATMENT (Tratamiento):

The patient needs to remain home until the sores are healed. Sores should be washed with soap and water to remove crusts. An application of antibiotic ointment should be applied as directed. If symptoms persist, a doctor should be consulted.

El paciente debe quedarse en casa hasta que se curen las úlceras. Las llagas se deben lavar con agua y jabón para quitarles las costras, y se debe aplicar un ungüento antibiótico según se indique. Si persisten los síntomas, hay que consultar a un médico.

Scabies
La Sarna

SYMPTOMS (Síntomas):

Small elevated spots caused by a microscopic mite that burrows into the skin. It is usually found between the fingers and toes, inside the elbow, behind the knee or in the crotch area. The patient suffers intense itching. It spreads easily in families and from close contact.

Vejiguillas causadas por un arácnido acárido microscópico que cava y vive dentro de la piel. Generalmente se encuentra entre los dedos de las manos y de los pies, el interior del codo, detrás de la rodilla o en la entrepierna. El (La) paciente sufre un vivo picor. La sarna se extiende fácilmente entre la familia y al tener contacto próximo con la persona infectada.

TREATMENT (Tratamiento):

A prescription medication is needed to treat this condition. The patient must remain out of school until the condition is adequately treated.

Se necesita tratar esta condición con un medicamento recetado. El (La) paciente debe quedarse en casa hasta que se cure.

Tuberculosis (TB)
Tuberculosis

SYMPTOMS (Síntomas):

Chronic coughing with sputum, fatigue and weakness, loss of appetite and weight, and spitting blood.
Tos crónica con esputo, fatiga y debilidad, falta de apetito, pérdida de peso y al escupir hay sangre en el esputo.

Sometimes a person can have TB without showing symptoms.
A veces se puede tener la tuberculosis sin que se manifiesten síntomas.

METHOD OF TRANSFER (Forma de Contagio):

Breathing the TB germ. (It is not hereditary.)
Respirando los gérmenes de la tuberculosis. (No es hereditaria.)

Tests for TB:
Pruebas para la Tuberculosis

1. Tuberculin Test: a skin test done on the arm. It feels like a prick with a needle. It is necessary to have a doctor or nurse check it for a possible reaction two days later. The test shows if the TB germ is in the body.

1. **Prueba Tuberculina: una prueba que se hace en la piel del brazo. Se siente como un pinchazo de alfiler. Después que se ha hecho la prueba tuberculina, se debe ir al médico o a la enfermera en dos días para que vean la posible reacción. Ellos podrán decirle si la prueba indica que tiene gérmenes de la tuberculosis en su cuerpo.**

2. Chest X-Ray: a photograph of the lungs. It shows if the TB germs have damaged the lungs.

2. **Rayos X del pecho: Una fotografía de los pulmones. Indica si los microbios de la tuberculosis han dañado los pulmones.**

TREATMENT (Tratamiento):

Patients need to be seen for skin test and/or X-ray for diagnosis. TB is easily treated with appropriate medication, but the patient must remain on medication for a long period of time.
Los pacientes deben ir a un médico para una prueba tuberculina y /o de rayos X y así obtener un diagnóstico. La tuberculosis se trata fácilmente con el medicamento apropiado, pero el (la) paciente tiene que tomar el medicamento por mucho tiempo.

Venereal Diseases

Gonorrhea
La Gonorrea

SYMPTOMS (Síntomas):

Women: Inflamation of the pelvis. If a woman has been exposed there may not be obvious symptoms. Gonorrhea is sometimes not discovered in a woman until she has infected other sexual partners. If any symptom occurs it would probably be in the form of a thick discharge of pus from the cervix.

Mujeres: Inflamación de la pelvis. Puede ser que una mujer que haya sido expuesta a la enfermedad no tenga síntomas obvios. Muy a menudo, la gonorrea no se descubre en una mujer hasta que ella ha infectado a aquéllos con los que ha tenido relaciones sexuales. Si se manifestara algún síntoma, probablemente sería en la forma de una supuración espesa de pus de la cerviz.

Men: Inflamation of the testicles, discharge of pus from the penis; a painful burning sensation while urinating. If the disease is spread by oral or anal sex there may be no symptoms. Oral sexual exposure can result in a painful irritation of the throat; in the case of anal contact, a discharge of pus during defecation.

Hombres - Inflamación de los testículos, una supuración de pus del pene, una dolorosa sensación de ardor al orinar. Si la enfermedad se ha propagado por medio del coito oral o anal, se puede no tener ningún síntoma. Si algunos síntomas aparecieran a causa de haber tenido coito oral o anal, a menudo pueden aparecer en forma de una irritación muy dolorosa de la garganta o, en caso de contagio anal, un supuración de pus ocurre durante la defecación.

TREATMENT (Tratamiento):

Medical diagnosis and antibiotic treatment are essential to prevent serious complications. The patient must abstain from sexual relations until cleared by the doctor.
Diagnostico médico y tratamiento con antibióticos son esenciales para prevenir complicaciones serias. El (La) paciente tiene que abstenerse de relaciones sexuales hasta recibir permiso del médico.

Syphilis
Sífilis

A contagious disease that can attack and damage any tissue or organ of the body, especially the brain, heart, liver, and bones.
Una enfermedad contagiosa que puede atacar y dañar cualquier tejido u órgano del cuerpo, especialmente el cerebro, el corazón, el hígado y los huesos.

SYMPTOMS (**Síntomas**):

The first symptom is the appearance of a sore, called a chancre, which can appear within three weeks in or around the sexual organs. It can appear in the vagina, mouth or rectum where it is difficult to observe. Sometimes the chancre does not appear at all.
El primer síntoma de la sífilis es la aparición de una llaga llamada un chancro, que puede aparecer dentro de tres semanas en o alrededor de los órganos sexuales. Puede aparecer en la vagina, boca o recto, donde es difícil ser observado. A veces no aparece el chancro.

METHOD OF TRANSFER (**Forma de Contagio**):

Syphilis is spread through coitus or other types of intimate relations. Very often it is spread through contact with the chancre.
La sífilis se puede propagar por medio del coito u otros tipos de relaciones íntimas. Muy a menudo se puede propagar por contacto con el chancro.

TREATMENT (**Tratamiento**):

Medical diagnosis and antibiotic treatment are essential to prevent serious complications.
Diagnóstico médico y tratamiento con antibióticos se necesitan para prevenir complicaciones serias.

Dear Parents or Guardians: Date: ____________

Today we became aware of a case of head lice in your child's classroom. During our inspection of the students we discovered evidence of this condition with your child. To prevent the further spread of this condition, we must exclude your child from school until he/she has been adequately treated and free from all lice and eggs (nits).

Head lice are extremely small, brown, black or grayish-white insects and can barely be seen. The eggs are attached to the hair follicle and look like a clear, tiny dewdrop. They usually are found at the back of the neck at the hairline and behind the ears. Eggs are attached very tightly and must be removed with a fine comb or your fingernails.

In order to treat your child, it is important to follow the recommendations below very carefully.

1. A special shampoo is required. Ask your druggist or doctor to suggest one.

2. Follow instructions on the container EXACTLY. These shampoos kill the lice and loosen the nits or eggs, so they may be combed out or removed by sliding off the hair between the fingers. Rinsing the hair with equal parts vinegar and water will make it easier to remove the eggs.

3. Check all family members, and treat them if there is any sign of lice.

4. More than one treatment will probably be necessary. Be sure to follow the instructions exactly.

5. It is important to disinfect all objects and clothing that are used near the hair, such as bedding, combs, jackets, hats, stuffed animals, etc. Hot water and laundry detergent or dry cleaning will work. Stuffed toys can be put into securely tied plastic bags and put away for three to four weeks.

6. Vacuum the house thoroughly, especially the mattresses, pillows and around beds. Vacuum upholstered furniture. In cases of family infestation, spray all furniture and other items that cannot be washed or dry cleaned (such as car seats) with a spray recommended by your druggist.

The lice can live off the hair for ten or more days, so it is important that all these things be done **on the same** day to prevent reinfestation.

We are sorry, but we cannot allow your child to return to school until the treatment is complete and no more lice or eggs exist. This is necessary to protect all children enrolled in our schools.

Please bring your child to the nurse's office to be checked before being readmitted to school.

Thank you for your understanding and cooperation. When we work together, we help all children.

The School Nurse

Phone: ____________

Estimados Padres o Tutores: Fecha: ____________

Hoy nos dimos cuenta de un caso de piojos en la clase de su niño(a) y durante nuestra inspección de los estudiantes, descubrimos evidencia de esta condición en su niño(a). Para prevenir la difusión de esta condición, será necesario excluir a su niño(a) de la escuela hasta que tenga tratamiento adecuado y esté libre de todos los piojos y los huevecillos.

Los piojos del pelo son extremadamente pequeños, marrones, negros o de color blancuzco-grisáceo y casi no se ven. Los huevos se pegan al folículo del pelo y se parecen a una pequeña y transparente gota de rocío. Muchas veces se ven detrás de la nuca en la línea del pelo y detrás de los oídos. Los huevos se pegan fuertemente y se deben de quitar con peine espeso o las uñas.

Para dar tratamiento a su niño(a), favor de seguir las siguientes recomendaciones con mucho cuidado.

1. Un champú especial es requerido. Pídale al médico o al farmacéutico una recomendación.

2. Siga las instrucciones en el envase EXACTAMENTE. Estos champús matan los piojos y sueltan los huevecillos para que puedan sacarse del pelo con el peine o haciendo resbalar los dedos entre el pelo. Enjuagando el pelo con partes iguales de vinagre y agua facilita el quitarse los huevecillos.

3. Revise a todos los miembros de la familia y sométalos a tratamiento si hay evidencia de piojos.

4. Más de un tratamiento probablemente será necesario. Siga las instrucciones exactamente.

5. Es importante desinfectar todos los objetos y ropa usados cerca del pelo como ropa de cama, peines, chamarras, sombreros, juguetes de peluche, etc. Agua caliente y jabón para la ropa o limpiado en la tintorería es suficiente. Se pueden meter los juguetes de peluche en bolsas de plástico herméticamente cerradas de tres a cuatro semanas.

6. Limpie la casa a fondo con aspiradora, especialmente los colchones, almohadas, y alrededor de las camas. Limpie con aspiradora los muebles tapizados. En casos de infestación de la familia entera, rocíe con un desinfectante recomendado por la farmacia todos los muebles y otras cosas que no se puedan lavar o mandar a la tintorería (como asientos de carros).

Es importante que todas estas cosas se hagan **el mismo día** para prevenir reinfestación, porque los piojos pueden vivir fuera del pelo diez días o más.

El niño(a) no puede volver a la escuela hasta que el tratamiento sea completado y no existan más piojos o huevecillos. Lo sentimos, pero es para el bien de todos los estudiantes en nuestras escuelas.

Por favor traiga a su niño(a) a la oficina de la enfermera para revisarlo(la) antes de readmitirlo(la) a la escuela.

Gracias por su comprension y cooperación. Con mutua cooperación podemos ayudar a todos los niños.

La Enfermera Escolar

Teléfono: ____________

Dear Parents or Guardians:

Head lice (pediculosis) continues to be a problem at our school. We are keeping a close watch in classes where we know children have been exposed. We need your help in preventing the spread of head lice. Inspect your own child's hair at least once a week. If you suspect your child may have nits (the eggs) or lice, please notify the school immediately. Prompt treatment of all known cases is essential for the control of this problem.

School staff will continue inspecting children in classes where there is a known head lice problem, and we will continue to exclude all students who are found to have head lice. As always, all excluded children will be examined before they are permitted to return to class.

Head lice can happen to anyone. Only prompt adequate treatment will prevent its spread.

The School Nurse

Estimados Padres o Tutores:

Piojos, también llamados pediculosis, continúa siendo un problema en nuestra escuela. Estamos tratando de vigilar bien en clases donde hay niños que han sido expuestos a la contaminación. Necesitamos su ayuda para impedir la propagación de los piojos. Hagan una inspección del cabello de su hijo(a) por lo menos una vez por semana. Si ustedes sospechan que su hijo(a) tiene liendres (los huevos) o piojos, por favor notifíquenlo a la escuela inmediatamente. Tratamiento inmediato de todos los casos es esencial para el control de este problema.

El personal de la escuela continuará inspecciones de todos los niños en las clases donde hay una infestación. Excluimos de la escuela a todos los niños que tengan piojos. Como siempre, reexaminamos a todos los niños que han sido excluidos antes de darles permiso para regresar a la escuela.

Los piojos pueden afectar a cualquier persona. Tratamiento adecuado e inmediato es la única forma de prevenir la infestación.

La Enfermera Escolar

Communicable Disease Information

To Parents or Guardians: Date: ____________

The disease(s) checked below are now occurring in your child's school, and your child may have been exposed. You may want to call your doctor if any of the symptoms listed below appear. Everyone is better protected when an ill child is kept at home while contagious. It is especially important for your child's health that home care continue until his/her temperature is normal for 24 hours and symptoms have disappeared. Other children who have come in contact with the ill child may attend school as long as they are not ill.

___ **Chicken Pox:** Small water blisters on the scalp, neck and covered parts of the body are usually the first sign. The blisters break easily. A child may become cross, tire easily and have a fever during the first few days of the illness. A sick youngster should be kept at home for seven days from the appearance of the first crop of blisters. The incubation period* is 14 to 21 days.

___ **German Measles:** Common symptoms of this disease are a light rash and a swelling of the glands behind the ears and at the back of the neck. A sick student should be kept at home for at least four days after the rash first appears. The incubation period* is 14 to 21 days.

___ **Measles (Rubella):** A runny nose, sneezing, coughing, watery eyes and fever are the first symptoms. A blotchy rash appears about the fourth day. An ill child should be kept home for at least seven days after the rash appears. Ask your doctor about getting gamma globulin shots to protect others in the house who have not had the measles or been vaccinated against it. The disease can cause serious complications. The incubation period* is eight to thirteen days.

___ **Mumps:** Symptoms are a swelling and tenderness in front of and below the ear or under the jaw. It may be painful to move the jaw. An ill youngster should be kept at home for nine days from the start of swelling or less if swelling has subsided. The incubation period* is 12 to 26 days.

___ **Streptococcal Infection or Scarlet Fever:** This disease begins suddenly with vomiting, fever, sore throat and headache. A bright rash usually appears within 24 hours. The rash may not appear, but the disease is just as serious. If your child has these symptoms, call your doctor. If the child is receiving treatment with an effective antibiotic, isolation may be discontinued 24 hours after treatment is begun. If not receiving antibiotic, the child should be isolated for at least seven days from beginning of disease and until all signs completely disappear. The incubation period* is one to three days.

___ **Whooping Cough (Pertussis):** The main symptom is a persistent cough that comes in spells and ends in a whooping sound. However, many cases may have the persistent cough without the whooping sound. The coughing may cause vomiting. The disease is especially serious for infants. Without appropriate antibiotic treatment, your child can infect others from seven days after exposure to three weeks after start of typical cough. Communicability lasts for five to seven days after effective antibiotic treatment is started. The incubation period* is seven to ten days but could be as long as 21 days.

Please remember, whooping cough, diphtheria, tetanus, polio, German measles, measles and mumps can be prevented by immunization.

*Incubation period means the time it takes for the disease to develop after the child has been exposed.

Información Sobre Enfermedades Contagiosas

A Los Padres o Tutores: Fecha: ____________

Las enfermedades marcadas abajo están manifestándose en la escuela y su niño ha estado expuesto. Sería buena idea llamar al médico si alguno de los síntomas que se mencionan a continuación aparece en su niño(a). Para la protección del niño enfermo y de sus compañeros, es mejor que permanezca en su casa durante el tiempo en que la enfermedad es contagiosa. Es muy importante para la salud de su niño(a) que se continúe el cuidado en casa hasta que su temperatura permanezca a nivel normal por más de 24 horas y los síntomas hayan desaparecido. Otros niños que han estado en contacto con el niño enfermo pueden ir a la escuela mientras ellos no estén enfermos.

___ **Viruelas Locas:** Pequeñas ampollas de agua en la cabeza, cuello y partes cubiertas del cuerpo son generalmente las primeras señales de la enfermedad. Las ampollas se rompen fácilmente. El niño se pone de mal humor, se cansa pronto y tiene fiebre durante los primeros días de la enfermedad. El niño enfermo deberá permanecer en casa siete días después de que aparezcan las primeras ampollas. El período de incubación* de las viruelas locas es de 14 a 21 días.

___ **Rubéola o Sarampión Alemán:** Los síntomas comunes de esta enfermedad son un sarpullido o irritación de la piel así como una hinchazón de las glándulas detrás de los oídos y la parte posterior del cuello. El estudiante enfermo deberá permanecer en casa un mínimo de cuatro días después del primer síntoma de la enfermedad. El período de incubación* es de 14 a 21 días.

___ **Rubella o Sarampión:** (Sarampión de 10 días) - Nariz mucosa, estornudos, tos, ojos acuosos y fiebre son los síntomas iniciales. Ronchas de sarpullido aparecen cerca del cuarto día. El niño enfermo deberá permanecer en casa un mínimo de siete días después de la aparición del sarpullido. Consulte a su médico acerca de la posibilidad de recibir inyecciones de "gamma globulina" para proteger a los demás miembros de la familia que no han sido vacunados o que nunca han contraído la enfermedad. Esta enfermedad puede causar serias complicaciones. El período de incubación* es de ocho a trece días.

___ **Paperas:** Los síntomas son hinchazón y sensibilidad enfrente y detrás del oído o bajo la quijada. Puede ser doloroso mover la quijada. El niño enfermo deberá permanecer en casa un mínimo de nueve días desde la fecha en que aparecieron los primeros síntomas, o menos, si la inflamación ha bajado. El período de incubación* es de 12 a 26 días.

___ **Infección Estreptococal o Fiebre Escarlatina:** Esta enfermedad comienza inesperadamente con vómito, fiebre, dolor de garganta y dolor de cabeza. Generalmente aparece un brillante sarpullido en 24 horas. Aunque no tenga el sarpullido la enfermedad es igual de seria. Si su niño tiene estos síntomas consulte a su médico. Si al niño enfermo se le está dando un efectivo antibiótico se puede descontinuar el tener que mantenerlo aislado después de 24 horas de haber empezado el tratamiento. Si no está recibiendo antibióticos, se le deberá mantener aislado por un mínimo de siete días desde la fecha en que empezó la enfermedad hasta que las señales y los síntomas desaparezcan completamente. El período de incubación* es de uno a tres días.

___ **Tos Ferina (Pertusis):** El síntoma más importante es una tos convulsiva. En muchos casos se puede tener solamente una tos persistente sin ser convulsiva. La tos puede causar vómito. <u>La enfermedad es muy seria en los bebés</u>. Si no ha recibido tratamiento con antibióticos, el período contagioso se extiende de siete días después del contagio hasta tres semanas después de declararse la enfermedad. El período de contagio es de cinco a siete días de la fecha en que empezó el tratamiento con antibióticos. El período de incubación es de siete a diez días, pero puede ser de hasta 21 días.

¡Recuerde! Tos ferina, difteria, tétano, polio, rubéola, rubella (o sarampión) y paperas se pueden prevenir con vacunas.

*El período de incubación se refiere al tiempo que tarda la enfermedad en aparecer después del contacto infeccioso.

Dental Health

Communicating with Students

1. Please open your mouth.
   Abre la boca, por favor.

2. Point to where it hurts.
   Indícame dónde te duele.

3. Did you lose a tooth?
   ¿Se te ha caído un diente?

4. Do your gums bleed when you brush your teeth?
   ¿Te sangran las encías cuando te cepillas los dientes?

5. Do you brush your teeth every day?
   ¿Te cepillas los dientes todos los días?

6. Do you have a toothbrush?
   ¿Tienes cepillo de dientes?

7. Do you have toothpaste or tooth powder?
   ¿Tienes pasta dental o polvo dentífrico?

8. If you don't have toothpaste or tooth powder you can brush without them or use baking soda.
   Si no tienes pasta dental o polvo dentífrico, puedes cepillarte los dientes sin nada o usar bicarbonato de soda.

9. A fluoride toothpaste helps prevent cavities.
Una crema dental que contiene fluoruro ayuda a prevenir la formación de las caries dentales.

10. A mouthwash does not remove plaque, prevent cavities or prevent gum disease.
Un enjuague bucal no quita la placa ni evita las caries ni las enfermedades en las encías.

11. Bad breath can indicate dental or other kinds of illnesses.
El mal aliento puede indicar una salud dental deficiente u otras clases de enfermedades.

12. Do you eat a lot of candy?
¿Comes muchos dulces?

13. You need to use dental floss every day.
Necesitas usar hilo dental todos los días.

14. Here is a picture of how to floss.
Aquí tienes una foto de cómo usar el hilo dental.

15. Here is a picture of how to brush your teeth.
Aquí tienes una foto de cómo cepillarte los dientes.

16. How did you break your tooth?
¿Cómo te rompiste el diente?

17. How long has it been broken?
¿Desde cuándo tiempo ha estado roto?

18. When did you last see a dentist? This year? Last year?
¿Cuándo viste a un dentista la última vez? ¿Este año? ¿El año pasado?

19. Did the dentist clean your teeth?
¿Te limpió los dientes el dentista?

20. Did the dentist fill your cavities?
¿Te empastó el dentista las picaduras (caries)?

Communicating with Parents

1. ______________ has a toothache.
   ______________ **tiene dolor de dientes.**

2. ______________ broke a tooth and needs to see a dentist immediately.
   ______________ **se rompió un diente y necesita ir a un dentista inmediatamente.**

3. ______________ has a cavity (cavities).
   ______________ **tiene una carie (unas caries).**

4. ______________ has plaque.
   ______________ **tiene placa.**

5. ______________ needs to brush his (her) teeth two or three times a day.
   ______________ **necesita cepillarse los dientes dos o tres veces al día.**

6. Your child has poor dental health because he (she) is not brushing his (her) teeth regularly.
   Su niño(a) tiene mala salubridad dental porque no se cepilla los dientes regularmente.

7. Does your child (Do your children) have a toothbrush?
   ¿Tiene (Tienen) su niño(a) (sus niños) cepillo para los dientes?

8. I have a toothbrush (toothbrushes) for your child(ren).
   Tengo un cepillo (cepillos) para su niño(a) (sus niños).

9. Your child will need a new toothbrush from time to time.
   Su niño(a) necesitará un cepillo nuevo de vez en cuando.

10. Brushing one's teeth removes plaque (dangerous bacteria which constantly forms on the teeth).
    El cepillarse los dientes quita la placa (bacteria peligrosa que se forma constantemente en los dientes).

11. Plaque accumulates and becomes tartar which can only be removed by a dentist or a dental hygienist.
    La placa se acumula y se convierte en un depósito duro que se llama sarro de los dientes (tártaro), que sólo lo puede quitar el dentista o un higienista dental.

12. Plaque causes dental illnesses. It causes cavities and periodontal disease.
    La placa causa enfermedades dentales. Causa caries y enfermedad periodontal.

13. Please show your child(ren) how to use dental floss.
    Favor de mostrarle a su niño(a) (sus niños) cómo usar el hilo dental.

14. Your child needs to floss at least once a day to keep plaque under control.
    Su niño(a) necesita usar el hilo dental por lo menos una vez al día para mantener la placa bajo control.

15. After brushing and flossing it is necessary to rinse the mouth out with water.
Después de haberse cepillado los dientes y usado el hilo dental, hay que enjuagarse la boca con agua.

16. People feel better when their mouths are clean.
Uno se siente mejor cuando tiene la boca limpia.

17. Cavities can cause children to lose teeth.
Las caries pueden ocasionar la pérdida de dientes a los niños.

18. Candy causes cavities.
Los dulces causan caries.

19. Children should not eat a lot of candy, or foods containing sugar.
Los niños no deben comer muchos dulces, o comidas que contienen azúcar.

20. Decayed teeth can cause infections in other parts of the body.
Los dientes picados pueden ocasionar infecciones en otras partes del cuerpo.

21. When did __________ last see a dentist? Last year? This year?
¿Cuándo vio __________ a un dentista la última vez? ¿El año pasado? ¿Este año?

22. Please contact the clinic for dental services. You may need to make an appointment in advance.
Por favor, llame a la clínica de servicios dentales. Es posible que necesite hacer una cita con anticipación.

23. They charge on ability to pay.
Le cobrarán según su abilidad de pagar.

24. The telephone number is__________________.
El número de teléfono es __________________.

25. The address is ________________________.
La dirección es ________________________.

Dental Terminology

baby tooth	**el diente de leche**
braces	**los frenos para dientes**
breath	**el aliento**
breath, bad	**el mal aliento**
brush, to brush teeth	**cepillarse (lavarse) los dientes**
buck teeth	**los dientes salientes**
calcium	**el calcio**
candy	**los dulces** **los bombones** **los caramelos**
cavity	**la carie** **la picadura**
cavities	**las caries** **las picaduras**
to chew	**masticar**
chewing gum	**el chicle** **la goma de mascar**
to clean teeth	**limpiar los dientes**
decayed teeth	**los dientes picados**
dental health	**la salud dental**
dental hygienist	**el (la) higienista dental**
dentistry	**la odontología** **la dentistería**
floss	**el hilo dental**
fluoride	**el fluoruro**
gum, chewing	**la goma de mascar** **el chicle**
gum disease	**la enfermedad de las encías**
gums	**las encías**

jaw	**la quijada** **la mandíbula**
mouth	**la boca**
mouthwash	**el enjuague bucal** **el enjuague dental**
novocaine	**la novocaína** **la procaína**
orthodontist	**el (la) ortodontista**
periodontal illness	**la enfermedad periodontal**
plaque	**la placa**
prevention	**la prevención**
to rinse	**enjuagar**
root canal	**el canal de la raíz**
sweet tooth, to have a	**tener el gusto por los dulces** **ser goloso**
tartar	**el tártaro** **el cálculo**
teeth	**los dientes**
teeth, decayed	**los dientes picados**
teeth, false	**la dentadura postiza**
teething	**la dentición**
tongue	**la lengua**
tooth	**el diente**
toothache	**el dolor de dientes (muelas)**
toothbrush	**el cepillo de dientes**
toothpaste	**la crema dental** **el dentrífico**
toothpick	**el palillo de dientes**
tooth powder	**el polvo dentífrico**
wisdom tooth (teeth)	**la muela cordal** **la(s) muela(s) del juicio**

Name: ______________________________ Date: ____________

Age: _____ Teacher: ________________ School: ______________

Dear Parents or Guardians:

Your child was recently examined as part of the school's dental health program. The preliminary findings indicate:

___ Your child has no immediate problems at this time, but your child should see your family dentist every six months to keep his/her teeth in perfect dental health.

___ Your child has several teeth with cavities. Please see your family dentist.

___ Your child has very poor dental health. Please see your dentist immediately.

___ Orthodontic consultation needed.

Regardless of the present condition of your child's teeth, it is most important to seek professional dental care in order to:

1. Maintain the health of his/her mouth.
2. Correct any deformities before they become painful and expensive.
3. Teach your child how to maintain his/her teeth and mouth to last a lifetime with the least expense.

We encourage all parents to establish a regular dental program with a dentist or clinic in the area.

Thank you,

____
The School Nurse

Examining Dentist's Comments:

Nombre: ________________________________ Fecha: _______________

Edad: ____ Maestro(a): ________________ Escuela: ____________________

Estimados Padres o Tutores:

Su hijo/a ha sido examinado recientemente como parte del programa de salubridad dental de la escuela. La condición de la boca de su hijo/a es:

____ Su niño/a no tiene ningún problema dental, pero su niño/a debe ir al dentista cada seis meses para mantener su dentadura en perfectas condiciones de salubridad.

____ A su niño/a se le encontraron varias caries. Es necesario que vaya al dentista.

____ Su niño/a tiene mala dentadura. Es necesario que vaya al dentista inmediatamente.

____ Su niño/a requiere ser visto(a) por un especialista en ortodoncia.

De cualquier manera, es muy importante obtener cuidado dental profesional para poder:

1. Mantener la salud de su boca.
2. Corregir algunas deformidades antes de que sean dolorosas y caras.
3. Enseñar a su hijo/a cómo cuidar sus dientes para que le duren toda su vida y con el menor costo.

Se le aconseja establecer un programa dental regular con un(a) dentista en el área.

Atentamente,

____
La Enfermera Escolar

Examining Dentist's Comments:
(Comentarios del Dentista)

Nutrition

Questioning and Advising a Student

Eating Habits

1. What do you usually eat for breakfast (lunch, dinner)?
   ¿Qué comes generalmente para el desayuno (el almuerzo, la cena)?

2. How often do you eat _____________?
   ¿Con qué frecuencia comes _____________?

3. What do you usually eat between meals (before going to bed, while watching TV)?
   ¿Qué comes generalmente entre las comidas (antes de acostarte, mientras miras la tele)?

4. Do you bring your lunch to school?
   ¿Traes tu almuerzo a la escuela?

5. Do you drink coffee (alcohol, milk, soft drinks, tea)?
   ¿Tomas café (bebidas alcohólicas, leche, refrescos, té)?

6. How many glasses of water do you drink during the day?
   ¿Cuántos vasos de agua bebes durante el día?

7. Who prepares your food at home?
   ¿Quién te prepara la comida en casa?

Food Problems

1. What foods do you dislike?
   ¿Qué comida(s) no te gusta(n)?

2. Are you allergic to any foods?
   ¿Tienes alergia a alguna comida?

3. What are they?
   ¿Qué comidas son?

4. What kind of physical reaction do you have?
   ¿Qué tipo de reacción física tienes?

Diet and Exercise

1. Are you on any kind of special diet?
   ¿Estás a dieta especial?

2. Have you ever been on a diet before?
   ¿Has estado a dieta antes?

3. Have you followed the diet I gave you?
   ¿Has seguido la dieta que te di?

4. You will feel much better if you eat a proper diet and get some exercise.
   Te sentirás mucho mejor si comes una dieta apropiada y haces ejercicio.

5. A good diet is very important for participation in sports.
   Una buena dieta es muy importante si se hacen deportes.

Communicating with Parents

Nutrition

1. Does your child eat regular meals?
   ¿Come su hijo(a) comidas normales?

2. Does your child eat breakfast? Every day?
   ¿Desayuna su hijo(a)? ¿Todos los días?

3. What does your child eat for breakfast (lunch, dinner)?
   ¿Qué come su hijo(a) para el desayuno (el almuerzo, la cena)?

4. What did _______________ eat for breakfast this morning?
   ¿Qué comió _______________ para el desayuno esta mañana?

5. It is very important for your child to have a good breakfast before coming to school.
   Es muy importante que su hijo(a) desayune bien antes de venir a la escuela.

6. Do you know the school has a breakfast (lunch) program? It costs $_______ for breakfast and $________ for lunch.
   ¿Sabe usted que la escuela tiene un programa de desayuno (almuerzo)? Cuesta $_______ el desayuno y $_______ el almuerzo.

7. Your child may qualify for free breakfast (lunch). Please see the school secretary for an application.
   Quizás su hijo(a) pueda recibir desayunos (almuerzos) gratis. Por favor, pídale una solicitud a la secretaria de la escuela.

8. _________________ appears to have good (poor) nutrition.
   _________________ **parece tener buena (mala) nutrición.**

Diet

1. ______________ needs to follow a diet.
   ______________ **debe ponerse a dieta.**

2. Did the doctor give ______________ a special diet?
   ¿El médico le dio un régimen (una dieta) especial a ______________?

3. ______________ will be healthier if he (she) loses (gains) weight.
   ______________ **estaría en mejor forma si él (ella) perdiera (subiera) de peso).**

4. Be sure ______________ has low calorie meals each day.
   Asegúrese de que ______________ coma comidas de pocas calorías todos los días.

Substance Abuse

Questioning a Student About Drugs

1. Are you using drugs?
   ¿Tomas drogas?

2. Have these drugs been prescribed by your doctor?
   ¿Tu médico te las ha recetado?

3. What kind of drugs are you using?
   ¿Qué tipo de drogas usas?

4. How long have you been on drugs?
   ¿Desde cuándo tomas drogas?

5. Is someone giving you drugs?
   ¿Alguien te da drogas?

6. Who else is using drugs?
   ¿Quién más usa drogas?

7. Where are they buying them?
   ¿Dónde las compran?

8. Who is selling them?
   ¿Quién las vende?

9. Do you know the consequences of taking (selling) drugs?
¿Sabes las consecuencias de tomar (vender) drogas?

10. Do you know that you can be arrested?
¿Sabes que puedes ser arrestado?

11. Do you know that you can go to jail?
¿Sabes que puedes ir a la cárcel?

12. Do you know that there can be serious medical consequences from taking drugs?
¿Sabes que puede haber serias consecuencias médicas al tomar drogas?

13. Do you understand the dangers?
¿Comprendes los riesgos?

14. Do you understand the risks you are taking?
¿Comprendes los riesgos que corres?

15. Are you aware that students your age have died from drugs?
¿Te das cuenta de que alumnos de tu edad han muerto de usar drogas?

16. Have you ever been in a drug treatment program?
¿Has estado alguna vez en un programa de tratamiento de drogas?

17. Have you ever been arrested for having (using, selling) drugs?
¿Has sido alguna vez arrestado por tener (usar, vender) drogas?

Assistance

1. The school has a drug assistance program.
La escuela tiene un programa de ayuda a los que abusan del uso de las drogas.

2. We can help you.
Podemos ayudarte.

3. Do you want our help?
¿Quieres nuestra ayuda?

4. You can overcome drug dependency.
Puedes superar la dependencia de las drogas.

5. You can help others who are on drugs.
Puedes ayudar a otros que usan drogas.

6. They need your help.
   Necesitan tu ayuda.

7. What ideas do you have for keeping students away from drugs?
   ¿Qué ideas tienes para evitar que otros alumnos usen drogas?

8. What are the disadvantages of using drugs?
   ¿Cuáles son las desventajas de usar drogas?

9. I care about what's happening to you.
   Me importa lo que te está pasando.

10. We have a voluntary drug testing program here at school.
    Tenemos un programa voluntario de análisis, aquí en la escuela, para determinar si la persona usa drogas.

11. Your parents will need to come to school and meet with me.
    Tus padres van a tener que venir a la escuela y verme.

12. Your parents will need to fill out this form.
    Tus padres tendrán que llenar este impreso.

Questioning a Student About Drinking

1. Have you been drinking today?
   ¿Has estado tomando bebidas alcohólicas hoy?

2. What have you been drinking?
   ¿Qué has estado tomando?

3. How much?
   ¿Cuánto has tomado?

4. When did you take the last drink?
   ¿Cuándo tomaste el último trago?

5. Do your parents know you are drinking?
   ¿Saben tus padres que tomas?

6. Where are you getting it?
   ¿Dónde consigues las bebidas alcohólicas?

Questioning a Student About Smoking

1. Have you been smoking here at school?
   ¿Has estado fumando aquí en la escuela?

2. Do you have cigarettes with you?
   ¿Tienes cigarrillos contigo?

3. Please give them to me.
   Por favor, dámelos.

4. Smoking is very dangerous to your health.
   El fumar es muy peligroso para tu salud.

5. Smoking is not allowed on campus.
   No se permite fumar en la escuela.

6. I'll need to report this to the principal.
   Tendré que reportar esto al director.

7. I'll have to call your parents and discuss this with them.
   Tendré que llamar a tus padres y hablar con ellos acerca de esto.

Communicating with Parents

1. ___________ is here in my office and is under the influence of drugs (alcohol).
   ___________ **está aquí en mi oficina y está bajo la influencia de drogas (alcohol).**

2. ___________ was under the influence of drugs (alcohol) at school today.
   ___________ **estaba bajo la influencia de drogas (alcohol) en la escuela hoy.**

3. ___________ was smoking on campus today.
   ___________ **estaba fumando en la escuela hoy.**

4. This is the __________ time he (she) has been caught using drugs (drinking, smoking).
   Esta es la __________ vez que él (ella) ha sido sorprendido(a) usando drogas (tomando bebidas alcohólicas, fumando).

5. You will need to come to school and pick him (her) up.
   Usted tendrá que venir a la escuela a recogerlo(la).

6. You need to come to school and meet with me (the principal).
   Usted necesita venir a la escuela para hablar conmigo (con el director).

Substance Abuse Terminology

acid	**el ácido**
addict	**el (la) adicto(a)** **el (la) toxicómano(a)**
addict, to addict oneself	**enviciarse con** **entregarse a** **depender de**
addiction	**la adicción**
alcohol	**el alcohol**
alcoholic	**el (la) alcohólico(a)**
angel dust	**el polvo del ángel**
arrest	**detener** **arrestar**
cigarettes	**los cigarrillos** **los pitillos**
cocaine	**la cocaína** **la coca**
dope	**el narcótico**
drinker	**el (la) bebedor(a)**
drugs, to be mixed up in	**meterse en el mundo de las drogas**
drug addict	**el (la) toxicómano(a)** **el (la) drogadicto(a)**
drug addiction	**la toxicomanía**
drug habit	**el vicio de los narcóticos**
drug traffic	**el tráfico de drogas**
drunk, to be	**estar borracho(a)** **estar bebido(a)**
drunk driving	**conducir en estado de embriaguez**
drunk driving, to be arrested for	**ser detenido(a) por conducir en estado de embriaguez**
drunkenness	**la embriaguez** **la borrachera**

drunk, to be	**emborracharse**
hangover	**la cruda** **la resaca**
hangover, to have a	**estar crudo(a)** **estar con resaca**
heroin	**la heroína**
heroin user	**el que usa heroína**
inject, to	**inyectar**
injection	**la inyección**
intoxicated, to become	**embriagarse** **emborracharse**
liquor	**el licor**
marijuana	**la mariguana**
narcotics	**los narcóticos**
overdose	**la dosis excesiva**
pass out, to	**desmayarse**
PCP	**el polvo del ángel**
pep pill	**el estimulante**
pot	**la mariguana**
sleeping pills	**las píldoras para dormir**
smoke, to	**fumar**
sniff, to	**sorber por las narices**
steroids	**los esteroides**
stimulant	**el estimulante**
withdrawal symptoms	**el síndrome de la abstinencia**

Child Abuse

The inclusion of this chapter on child abuse in no way implies a higher incidence of child abuse among the Hispanic population than in the general population. This material is intended to assist school personnel in dealing with those instances in which child abuse is suspected.

Reporting Suspected Child Abuse

Most states have strict laws regulating the reporting of child abuse. In addition, most school districts have detailed policies outlining the steps to be taken by school personnel. Users of this book are referred to both state laws and district policies.

Talking with a Suspected Victim of Child Abuse

1. Please sit here.
   Por favor, siéntate aquí.

2. Don't be afraid.
   No tengas miedo. No temas.

3. I'm here to help you.
   Estoy aquí para ayudarte.

4. What do you want to talk with me about?
   ¿De qué quieres hablarme?

5. I notice you have a ___________ (describe injury).
   Veo que tienes un(a) ___________.

6. Your teacher told me you have something to show me.
   Tu maestro(a) me dijo que tienes algo que mostrarme.

7. Can you tell me what happened?
   ¿Puedes decirme lo que pasó?

8. What happened before that?
   ¿Qué pasó antes de eso?

9. Can you tell me more?
   ¿Qué más puedes decirme?

10. Was your (mother, father,) home at the time?
    ¿Estaba tu madre (padre) en casa en ese momento?

11. Where were you when it happened?
    ¿Dónde estabas cuando pasó?

12. Has this happened before?
    ¿Ha ocurrido esto antes?

13. You don't have to feel ashamed.
    No debes sentirte avergonzado(a).

14. You can tell me the whole story.
    Puedes contármelo todo.

15. You can trust me.
    Puedes confiar en mí.

16. Let me look at your injury.
    Déjame ver tu herida.

17. It's all right to cry.
Está bien llorar.

18. What about your brothers and sisters?
¿Qué les pasó a tus hermanos?

19. Are you afraid to go home?
¿Tienes miedo de volver a casa?

20. I will need to notify a social worker who will help you (and your parents).
Tendré que avisar a un(a) trabajador(a) social que te ayudará (y que ayudará a tus padres).

Community Resources

Agency	Telephone Number
Child Abuse Prevention Hotline	____________________ ____________________
Family Counseling Services	____________________ ____________________
Women's Resource Groups	____________________ ____________________
Local Law Enforcement	____________________ ____________________
County or State Social Service Agencies	____________________ ____________________
Other ______________________________ ______________________________	____________________ ____________________ ____________________ ____________________

Vocabulary

abandoned	**abandonado(a)**
abrasion(s)	**la abrasión (las abrasiones)**
abuse	**el abuso** **el maltrato** **la injuria**
abuse, to	**maltratar a** **injuriar a** **abusar de**
abusive	**abusivo(a)** **injurioso(a)** **insultante**
accuse, to	**acusar**
accusation	**la acusación**
afraid, to be	**tener miedo** **temer**
apprehensive	**aprensivo(a)** **temeroso(a)** **receloso(a)**
bruise(s)	**la contusión (las contusiones)**
burn(s)	**la (las) quemadura(s)**
child welfare	**la protección de la infancia**
coerce, to	**forzar**
confidentiality	**la confidencialidad**
criminal behavior	**la conducta criminal**
cruelty	**la crueldad**
emotional stress	**la tensión emocional**
endanger, to	**poner en peligro**
excessive	**excesivo(a)**
fondle, to	**acariciar**
foster home	**la familia adoptiva temporal** **el hogar adoptivo temporal** **la casa adoptiva temporal**

frightened, to be	**tener miedo** **temer**
genital penetration	**la penetración genital**
health, endangered	**la salud en peligro**
help	**la ayuda** **el socorro**
hygiene, poor	**la mala higiene**
incest	**el incesto**
injure, to	**hacer daño a** **lastimar a** **herir a**
injury	**la herida** **la lesión**
lewd acts	**las acciones obscenas** **las acciones impúdicas**
maltreat, to	**maltratar a**
molest, to	**vejar sexualmente** **aprovecharse sexualmente de alguien**
molestation	**la vejación sexual** **el aprovecharse sexualmente de alguien**
mental suffering	**el sufrimiento mental**
neglect, to	**descuidar** **desatender**
neglect	**la negligencia** **el descuido**
neglected	**desatendido(a)**
negligence	**la negligencia**
negligent	**negligente** **descuidado(a)**
obscene acts	**las acciones impúdicas** **las acciones indecentes** **las acciones obscenas**
physical pain	**el dolor físico**
physical punishment	**el castigo corporal** **el castigo físico**

private	**privado(a)**
psychological problems	**los problemas psicológicos**
punishment (unjustifiable) (excessive)	**el castigo (injustificable) (excesivo)**
rape	**la violación**
reasonable suspicion	**la sospecha razonable**
sexual abuse	**el abuso sexual**
sexual assault	**el asalto sexual**
sexual exploitation	**la explotación sexual**
suspected abuse	**el abuso sospechado**
suspicion(s)	**la(s) sospecha(s)**
suspect, to	**sospechar**
traumatic	**traumático(a)**
unattended physical problems	**los problemas físicos desatendidos**
uncared for	**mal cuidado(a) desatendido(a)**
unfit	**incapaz incompetente**
unjustifiable	**injustificable**
victim	**la víctima**
violate, to	**violar**
violate sexually, to	**violar sexualmente**
violence	**la violencia**
violent	**violento(a)**
welt(s)	**el verdugón los verdugones**
withdrawn	**reservado(a) introvertido(a)**

Communicating with Parents

General Questions

1. What is your name?
   ¿Cómo se llama usted? or **¿Cuál es su nombre?**

2. Are you the mother (father) of ______________?
   ¿Es usted la madre (el padre) de ______________?

3. Are you the parents of ______________?
   ¿Son ustedes los padres de ______________?

4. What is the child's first, middle and last name?
   ¿Cuál es el nombre de pila y apellidos del niño (de la niña)?

5. What is the child's date of birth?
   ¿Cuál es la fecha del nacimiento de su hijo(a)?

6. Where was he (she) born?
   ¿Dónde nació?

7. How many other children are there in the family?
   ¿Cuántos otros niños hay en la familia?

8. What are their names and ages?
   ¿Cuáles son sus nombres y edades?

9. Are both the mother and father living in the home?
   ¿Viven ambos padres en casa?

10. Do you have a telephone?
    ¿Tienen ustedes teléfono?

11. What is the number?
¿Cuál es el número?

12. Where do you live?
¿Dónde vive usted?

13. What is your address?
¿Cuál es su dirección?

14. What is your length of residence in the United States (in this county)?
¿Desde cuándo vive usted en los Estados Unidos (en este condado)?

15. Do you work outside the home?
¿Trabaja usted fuera de casa?

16. Does your husband (wife) work?
¿Trabaja su esposo (esposa)?

17. What is your occupation?
¿Cuál es la ocupación de usted?

18. What hours do you work?
¿Entre qué horas trabaja usted?

19. What is your husband's (wife's) occupation?
¿Cuál es la ocupación de su esposo (esposa)?

20. Are you dependent on public funds for support?
¿Depende usted de fondos públicos para sostenerse?

21. Are you on welfare or any other assistance program?
¿Recibe usted asistencia pública u otra asistencia?

22. Who takes care of your children when you work?
¿Quién cuida a sus hijos cuando usted trabaja?

23. How many people in the family work?
¿Cuántas personas en la familia tienen trabajo?

24. Is there anyone in your household who speaks English?
¿Hay alguien en su casa que hable inglés?

25. Do you have a neighbor or relative who speaks English?
¿Tiene un vecino o pariente que hable inglés?

26. What is his (her) name and telephone number?
¿Cuál es su nombre y número de teléfono?

27. How many persons live in the household including you and your child?
¿Cuántas personas viven en casa, incluyendo a usted y a su hijo(a)?

28. Are they all members of your family?
¿Todos son miembros de su familia?

29. How many bedrooms do you have?
¿Cuántos dormitorios tiene?

30. Do you have an indoor bathroom?
¿Tiene cuarto de baño dentro de la casa?

31. Do you have hot and cold running water?
¿Tiene agua corriente, caliente y fría?

32. Do you have any problems in the house (apartment) with insects or rodents?
¿Tiene problemas en la casa (apartamento) con insectos o roedores?

33. How many children are too young to attend school?
¿Cuántos niños son demasiado jóvenes para asistir a la escuela?

34. Who is your closest relative in the United States?
¿Quién es su pariente más cercano en los Estados Unidos?

35. Whom can we contact in case of an emergency?
¿A quién podemos llamar en caso de emergencia?

36. Is this person a relative, friend or neighbor?
¿Es esta persona un(a) pariente, amigo(a) o vecino(a)?

37. Where does this person live?
¿Dónde vive esta persona?

38. What is his (her) telephone number?
¿Cuál es el número de teléfono de él (ella)?

39. What relation are you to ______________?
¿Qué parentesco tiene usted con ____________?

Family Medical History

1. I have some questions about your family's and __________'s health that I want to ask you so we can better help him (her) at school.
Tengo algunas preguntas sobre la salud de su familia y de __________ para mejor poder ayudarlo(la) en la escuela.

2. Have any family members had any serious physical or mental health problems?
¿Han tenido algunos miembros de la familia problemas de salud, físicos o mentales serios?

3. Has anyone in your family had any of the following?
¿Hay alguien en su familia que haya padecido de

tuberculosis	**tuberculosis?**
heart disease	**enfermedad del corazón?**
cancer	**cáncer?**
high blood pressure	**alta tensión sanguínea?**
asthma	**asma?**
allergies	**alergias?**

4. Have any of your children died?
¿Se murió alguno de sus niños?

5. What were the circumstances?
¿Cuáles fueron las circunstancias?

6. At what age did the child die?
¿A qué edad se murió?

Pregnancy and Birth History

1. How often did you see a doctor while you were pregnant with __________?
¿Con qué frecuencia fue usted al doctor durante su embarazo con _________?

2. Did you have any of the following pregnancy complications?
¿Tuvo algunas de las siguientes complicaciones cuando estaba en estado?

anemia	**anemia**
bleeding	**hemorragia**
edema	**edema**
kidney disease	**enfermedad de los riñones**
infections	**infecciones**
Rh factor	**factor Rh**
measles	**sarampión**
German Measles	**rubéola**
prolonged labor	**parto prolongado**
emotional distress	**angustia emocional**
other complications	**otras complicaciones**

3. Were you given medicine for any of these medical problems?
¿Le dieron medicina para algunos de estos problemas médicos?

4. What medicine did they give you?
¿Qué medicinas le dieron?

5. Did you smoke or drink alcohol during your pregnancy?
¿Fumó o tomó bebidas alcohólicas durante su embarazo?

6. Did you take any drugs when you were pregnant? What were they?
¿Tomó drogas o medicinas cuando estaba embarazada? ¿Cuáles eran?

7. How many pregnancies have you had? Any miscarriages?
¿Cuántos embarazos ha tenido? ¿Algún aborto espontáneo?

8. What did _______ weigh at birth?
¿Cuánto pesó __________ al nacer?

9. Was ____________ born in a hospital? Where?
¿Nació ______________ en un hospital? ¿Dónde?

10. Was ____________ an Rh baby?
¿Fue ____________ un niño Rh?

11. Was your delivery normal or were there problems, such as premature or delayed delivery?
¿Fue un parto normal o tuvo problemas, como parto prematuro o parto prolongado?

12. Did your child have difficulty breathing at birth?
¿Tuvo su niño dificultad en respirar al nacer?

13. Was ____________ placed in an incubator or oxygen tent?
¿Pusieron a ______________ en una incubadora o tienda de oxígeno?

14. Was there anything unusual about or wrong with ____________ when he (she) was born?
¿Le pasó algo fuera de lo normal o hubo algo malo con ______________ cuando nació?

Postnatal History

1. Did you or your child have any complications or did the child have any deformities after the delivery?
¿Tuvo usted o su niño complicaciones o tuvo el niño deformidades después del parto?

2. Following birth, did the child experience any of the following problems?
¿Después del nacimiento sufrió el (la) niño(a) de alguno de estos problemas?

jaundice	**ictericia**
anemia	**anemia**
respiratory disease	**enfermedad respiratoria**
colic	**cólico**
convulsions	**convulsiones**
bruises	**contusiones (magulladuras, moretones)**

bleeding	**hemorragia**
malformation	**malformación, deformidad**
time in an incubator	**tiempo en una incubadora**
feeding problems	**problemas con tomar alimento**
Rh problems	**problemas de Rh**

3. What other problems did your child have during the first months?
¿Qué otros problemas tuvo su niño(a) durante los primeros meses?

4. Was a doctor consulted? What was done?
¿Consultó a un doctor? ¿Qué se hizo al respecto?

5. Did your child gain weight normally?
¿Su niño(a) aumentó de peso normalmente?

6. If not, what was the problem?
Si no, ¿cuál era el problema?

7. What did the doctor say?
¿Qué dijo el doctor?

Developmental and Health History

1. At what age did your child
¿A qué edad pudo su niño(a)

sit without support?	**sentarse sin ayuda?**
crawl?	**empezar a gatear?**
walk alone?	**caminar sin ayuda?**
stand alone?	**estar de pie sin ayuda?**
speak his first word?	**decir sus primeras palabras?**
use sentences?	**empezar a hacer frases?**
dress himself?	**vestirse sin ayuda?**
exercise bladder control?	**obtener control del orinar?**
exercise bowel control?	**obtener control de la evacuación del vientre?**
stop bed-wetting?	**dejar de orinarse en la cama?**

2. At what age did your child have any of the following illnesses or medical problems?
¿A qué edad tuvo su niño alguna de las siguientes enfermedades o problemas médicos?

abdominal problems	**problemas abdominales**
allergies to	**alergias a**
food	**comida**
medicines	**medicinas**
insect bites (bees, wasps, spiders, ants)	**picaduras de (abejas, avispas, arañas, hormigas)**
other type of allergy	**otro tipo de alergia**
anemia	**anemia**

asthma	**asma**
bladder problems	**problemas de la vejiga**
chicken pox	**viruela**
convulsions	**convulsiones**
ear infections	**infecciones del oído**
epilepsy	**epilepsia**
frequent colds	**resfriados frecuentes**
flu	**gripe, influenza**
hay fever	**fiebre del heno**
heart disease	**enfermedad del corazón**
high fever	**fiebre alta**
kidney problems	**problemas de los riñones**
measles	**sarampión**
German measles	**rubéola**
mumps	**paperas**
pneumonia	**pulmonía**
rheumatic fever	**fiebre reumática**
tantrums	**rabietas, berrinches**
throat infections	**infecciones de la garganta**
thumb sucking	**se chupa el dedo**
tonsillitis	**anginas, inflamación de las amígdalas**
tuberculosis	**tuberculosis**
whooping cough	**tos ferina**

3. Which of the above has your child been vaccinated for?
   ¿Contra cuál de lo arriba mencionado ha sido vacunado su hijo(a)?

4. May I see _____________'s papers?
   ¿Puedo ver los papeles de _______________?

5. I need to see _____________'s papers.
   Necesito ver los papeles de _______________ .

6. Does your child have eye problems? Please describe the problems.
   ¿Tiene su niño(a) problemas con los ojos? Describa los problemas, por favor.

7. Does your child have ear problems? Please describe the problems.
   ¿Tiene su niño(a) problemas con los oídos? Discriba los problemas, por favor.

8. Does _____________ speak clearly?
   ¿Habla _____________ claramente?

9. What language does your child speak most often at home?
   ¿Qué idioma habla su niño(a) con más frecuencia en casa?

10. When was the last time your child was examined by a doctor (visited a clinic)?
    ¿Cuándo fue la última vez que su niño(a) fue examinado(a) por un doctor (fue a una clínica)?

11. What is the name, address and telephone number of the doctor?
    ¿Cuál es el nombre, dirección y número de télefono del médico?

12. Why did he (she) go at that time?
¿Por qué fue esa vez?

13. Has your child had any injuries or accidents? Please explain.
¿Ha tenido su niño(a) heridas o accidentes? Favor de explicar.

14. Has your child had any blows to the head, serious burns or other accidents? If so, when?
¿Ha tenido su niño(a) golpes a la cabeza, quemaduras serias u otros accidentes? ¿Cuándo?

15. Has your child ever been in a hospital? What for?
¿Ha estado su niño(a) en el hospital alguna vez? ¿Para qué?

16. Has ____________ ever had any operations? What for?
¿Ha sido operado ____________? ¿De qué?

17. Is your child taking any medicine now?
¿Está tomando su niño(a) alguna medicina ahora?

18. What is it for?
¿Para qué es?

19. Does he (she) take it on a regular basis?
¿La toma regularmente?

20. Do you use any home remedies? What are they?
¿Usa usted tratamientos caseros? ¿Cuáles son?

21. What time does ______________ usually go to bed? Wake up?
¿A qué hora se acuesta __________ generalmente? ¿Se levanta a qué hora?

22. Does he (she) sleep well?
¿Duerme bien?

23. How many hours a night does he (she) sleep?
¿Cuántas horas duerme él (ella)?

24. Does _____________ have fears? What type?
¿Tiene _____________ temores? ¿De qué clase?

25. Does your child often feel depressed?
¿Su hijo(a) se siente deprimido(a) con frecuencia?

26. Has ______________ ever had a memory loss?
¿Ha tenido ____________ pérdida de memoria alguna vez?

27. Does your child show any of the following signs of stress or nervous disorder?
¿Muestra su niño algunas de las siguientes señales de tensión o trastorno nervioso?

crying frequently	**llora frecuentemente**
depression	**depresión**
fearfulness	**miedo**

nail biting	**se muerde las uñas**
nightmares	**pesadillas**
sleeplessness	**insomnio**
thumb sucking	**se chupa el dedo**
other nervous habits	**otros hábitos nerviosos**

28. Does your child regularly eat three meals a day?
¿Come su hijo(a) tres comidas al día regularmente?

29. What does he (she) usually eat for breakfast (lunch, dinner)?
¿Qué come usualmente para el desayuno (el almuerzo, la cena)?

30. Has he (she) gained or lost weight lately?
¿Ha aumentado de o perdido peso recientemente?

31. Has ______________ ever been a victim of child abuse?
¿Alguna vez ha sido víctima de abuso ______________?

32. What were the circumstances?
¿Cuáles eran las circunstancias?

33. How does ______________ get along with other children? With adults?
¿Cómo se lleva ______________ con otros niños? ¿Con adultos?

34. Is his (her) attention span short, long or average?
¿Presta él (ella) atención durante ratos cortos, largos o medianos?

35. Does ______________ follow your discipline rules?
¿Sigue ______________ las reglas de disciplina de usted(es)?

36. What type of discipline does your child respond to?
¿A qué tipo de disciplina responde su hijo(a)?

37. Is there anything in your child's medical history that would affect his (her) ability to learn?
¿Hay algo en la historia médica de su niño(a) que pueda afectar su habilidad de aprender?

38. What do you think caused the problem?
¿Qué cree usted que ha causado el problema?

39. How do you think we can help the child with this problem?
¿Qué cree usted que podemos hacer para ayudar al (a la) niño(a) con este problema?

40. Was there anyone in your family who
¿Hubo alguien en su familia que

had problems learning?	**tuvo dificultad en aprender?**
had problems reading?	**tuvo dificultad en leer?**
was in special classes in school?	**estuvo en clases especiales en la escuela?**

Communicating with Parents About Sick Children

Calling Parents About Sick Children

1. Good morning (afternoon). My name is ___________.
   Buenos días (Buenas tardes). Me llamo ___________.

2. I am the school nurse (principal, secretary).
   Soy la enfermera (director[a], secretaria) de la escuela.

3. I am calling from ___________ school.
   Le llamo de la escuela ___________.

4. Who am I speaking with?
   ¿Con quién hablo?

5. What is your name?
   ¿Cómo se llama usted? or **¿Cuál es su nombre?**

6. Do you speak English?
   ¿Habla usted inglés?

7. Are you ___________'s mother (father, sister, brother, baby-sitter)?
   ¿Es usted la mamá (el papá, la hermana, el hermano, la niñera de ______________?

8. I need to speak with you about ___________.
   Necesito hablar con usted sobre ___________.

9. Why was ___________ absent yesterday (last week)?
   ¿Por qué faltó ___________ ayer (la semana pasada)?

10. How long has ___________ been sick?
    ¿Cuánto tiempo hace que está enfermo(a) ___________ ?

11. Was he (she) sick? What does he (she) have?
    ¿Estuvo enfermo(a)? ¿Qué tiene?

12. Is ___________ taking any kind of medication?
    ¿Está tomando ___________ medicamentos?

13. What are ___________'s symptoms?
    ¿Qué síntomas tiene ___________?

14. What is his (her) temperature?
    ¿Qué temperatura tiene?

15. Has your child been seen by a doctor?
    ¿Lo ha visto a su hijo(a) el médico?

16. What did the doctor say?
¿Qué dijo el médico?

17. You need to consult your doctor or clinic each time your child has a problem like this.
Usted necesita consultar a su médico o clínica cada vez que su niño(a) tiene un problema como éste.

18. When will __________ return to school?
¿Cuándo va a regresar a la escuela _____________?

19. Please always call the school on the first day your child is absent.
The number is __________.
Por favor siempre llame a la escuela el primer día que su hijo(a) esté ausente.
El número es ___________.

20. I would like to make a home visit.
Me gustaría hacer una visita a su casa.

21. Will you be home at ____________ today?
¿Estará en casa a la(s) ________________ hoy?

Sending Sick Children Home

1. Your child is ill.
Su niño(a) está enfermo(a).

2. ___________ needs to go home at once.
___________ **tiene que irse a casa inmediatamente.**

3. ___________ has a fever (stomachache, headache, ___________).
___________ **tiene fiebre (dolor de estómago, dolor de cabeza, _________).**

4. Your child tells us he (she) came to school sick. How long has he (she) been sick?
Su niño(a) nos dice que vino enfermo(a) a la escuela. ¿Desde cuándo ha estado enfermo(a)?

5. ___________ should have stayed home today.
___________ **debería haberse quedado en casa hoy.**

6. ___________ needs to rest in bed.
___________ **necesita descansar en cama.**

7. ___________ needs to stay in bed until his (her) fever is gone.
___________ **necesita guardar cama hasta que no tenga fiebre.**

8. Can you or someone else come and pick him (her) up (as soon as possible)?
¿Puede usted, u otra persona, venir a recogerlo(la) (tan pronto como sea posible)?

9. Please come and pick up your child as soon as possible.
Favor de venir y recoger a su niño(a) tan pronto como sea posible.

10. He (She) will be waiting in the school office (nurse's office).
El (Ella) estará esperando en la oficina de la escuela (de la enfermera).

Sending Sick Children to School

1. Please don't send your children to school when they have any of the following symptoms:
Favor de no mandar a los niños a la escuela cuando tienen alguno de estos síntomas:

fever	**fiebre**
diarrhea	**diarrea**
sore throat	**dolor de garganta**
infected throat	**infección de garganta**
dizziness or nausea	**mareos o vómitos**
head lice (nits)	**piojos (liendres)**
cold	**resfriado**
cough	**tos**
swollen eyes	**ojos inflamados**
skin rash	**erupción en la piel**
tonsillitis	**anginas inflamadas**
contagious diseases	**enfermedades contagiosas**

2. When children don't feel well they don't learn well.
Cuando los niños no se sienten bien no aprenden bien.

3. When your child comes to school sick, he (she) could be infecting other children.
Cuando su hijo(a) viene a la escuela enfermo(a), él (ella) puede infectar a otros niños.

Accidents and Injuries

1. Your child has had an accident.
Su hijo(a) ha tenido un accidente.

2. We don't think it is serious.
No creemos que sea serio.

3. It may be serious.
Puede ser serio.

4. __________ has a bump on the head and needs to be seen by a doctor or be observed at home. Be looking for anything unusual during the next 24 hours.
______ tiene un bulto en la cabeza y necesita ser visto por un médico o ser observado en casa. Esté a la mira de algo fuera de lo común por las próximas 24 horas.

5. Your child has an injury and needs to see a doctor as soon as possible.
Su niño(a) tiene una herida y necesita ir al médico tan pronto como sea posible.

6. Your child may have a broken bone in his (her) ____________. *
Es posible que su hijo(a) tenga un hueso roto en su ____________.

7. ___________________ fell off the swing (slide, bars) and is injured.
___________________ se cayó del columpio (resbaladero, barras) y está herido.

8. Your child has been stung by a bee.
Una abeja le ha picado a su hijo(a).

9. Has _______________ had a bee sting before? What was the reaction?
¿Ha sido picado ____________ por una abeja antes? ¿Cuál fue su reacción?

    local swelling? **¿hinchazón local?**

    problems breathing? **¿dificultad en respirar?**

10. Did you take your child to a doctor? What did the doctor say?
¿Llevó usted a su hijo(a) al médico? ¿Qué dijo el médico ?

* Please see page 93 for "The Body and Bodily Functions."

Bladder Control

1. _______________ has wet his (her) pants at school and will need a change of clothing.
   _______________ se ha mojado los pantalones en la escuela y va a necesitar ropa limpia.

2. _______________ will be waiting for you in the nurse's office.
   _______________ le estará esperando en la oficina de la enfermera.

3. Have you noticed that your child has this problem frequently? How often?
   ¿Ha notado usted que su hijo(a) tenga a menudo este problema? ¿Con qué frecuencia?

4. Is your child a bed wetter?
   ¿Moja su hijo(a) su cama?

5. Have you consulted a doctor about this problem?
   ¿Ha consultado usted a un médico acerca de este problema?

6. I would suggest that you take ____________ in for an examination.
   Sugiero que usted lleve a ______________ para que sea examinado(a).

Contagious Diseases

1. Your child has head lice (chicken pox, measles) and cannot return to school until the symptoms have disappeared.
   Su niño(a) tiene piojos (varicela, sarampión) y no puede regresar a la clase hasta que los síntomas hayan desaparecido.

2. You need to shampoo your child's hair with a special shampoo for head lice. You can buy it at the pharmacy.
   Usted necesita lavarle el pelo a su hijo(a) con un champú especial para los piojos. Usted puede comprarlo en la farmacia.

3. I am sending a letter home explaining what needs to be done before ________ can return to school.
   Le mando una carta a su casa en la que explico lo que se debe hacer antes de que _________ puede volver a la escuela.

4. You will need a note from the doctor or clinic stating that your child no longer has a contagious disease.
   Usted va a necesitar una nota del médico o de la clínica que indique que su hijo(a) ya no tiene una enfermedad contagiosa.

Seeking Medical Treatment

1. You must take your child to a doctor or clinic.
   Necesita llevar a su niño(a) al doctor o clínica.

2. The address is: ______________________________.
   La dirección es: ______________________________.

3. The telephone number is: __________________.
   El número de teléfono es: __________________.

4. The clinic hours are from __________ to __________.
   La clínica está abierta de __________ a __________.

5. There is a small charge at the clinic.
   Se cobra una pequeña cantidad por los servicios de la clínica.

6. The clinic does not charge for services.
   La clínica no cobra por los servicios.

7. Please call first for an appointment.
   Llame primero para hacer una cita.

8. You had better take your child to a doctor immediately.
   Tiene que llevar a su niño(a) al médico inmediatamente.

9. A consultation with a doctor may be expensive.
   La consulta con un médico puede ser cara.

10. Do you have insurance?
    ¿Tiene seguro?

11. Do you have the money to pay the bill?
    ¿Tiene el dinero suficiente para pagar la cuenta?

12. Consult your doctor or clinic each time your child has this problem.
    Consulte a su médico o clínica cada vez que su hijo(a) tenga este problema.

Readmission to School

1. Your child cannot return to school until he (she) is seen by a doctor or a clinic.
Su niño(a) no puede regresar a la escuela hasta que vaya al doctor o a la clínica.

2. We will need a note from the doctor or clinic that your child no longer has ____________. *
Vamos a necesitar una nota del médico o de la clínica que nos indique que su niño(a) ya no tiene ______________.

3. Keep your child home at least one full day after a fever or vomiting.
Que su niño(a) se quede en casa por lo menos un día entero después de una calentura o vómitos.

4. Send the doctor's diagnosis and recommended treatment to the school so the nurse can assist in caring for the needs of the child.
Mande a la escuela el diagnóstico del médico y el tratamiento que recomienda, para que así la enfermera pueda ayudar a cuidar a su hijo(a).

Medicine at School

1. Please let us know if your child has to take medicine at school.
Por favor infórmenos si su hijo(a) necesita tomar medicina en la escuela.

2. You need to bring us the medicine in the original bottle with the doctor's written directions.
Usted tiene que traernos la medicina, en el envase original, con las instrucciones del médico.

3. The school has a form for the doctor to fill out authorizing administration of medicine at school.
La escuela tiene un impreso que el médico deberá rellenar, autorizando el que le demos la medicina a su hijo(a) en la escuela.

4. The medicine, whether prescription or "over the counter," must be in its original container. We cannot accept medicine in plastic bags or envelopes.
La medicina, sea de receta o que no necesite receta, debe estar en el envase original. No podemos aceptar medicina en bolsas de plástico o sobres.

5. We must have your written permission to give the medicine to your child.
Necesitamos tener su permiso por escrito para poderle dar la medicina a su hijo(a).

* Please refer to page 100 for "Medical Conditions, Symptoms and Diseases."

6. Medicine is always dispensed in the nurse's (school) office by a designated school employee.
La medicina siempre se da en la oficina de la enfermera (escuela) por un empleado designado al respecto.

7. Your child will have to come to the office to take the medicine.
Su hijo(a) tendrá que venir a la oficina para tomar la medicina.

8. Medicine is not allowed in the classroom.
No se permite tener la medicina en la clase.

9. ______________ refuses to take his (her) medicine at school.
______________ **se niega a tomar su medicina en la escuela.**

Health Forms and Immunizations

1. Please fill out this health form giving your child's medical history, childhood diseases and immunization dates.
   Por favor rellene este impreso sobre la salud de su hijo(a), dando detalles del historial médico del niño(a), enfermedades de la niñez y fechas de las inmunizaciones (vacunas) por él (ella) recibidas.

2. If you have a personal or religious objection to the immunization of your child, sign here.
   Si usted tiene alguna objeción personal o religiosa en contra de la inmunización de su hijo(a), firme aquí.

3. Does you child have any special health problems such as diabetes, epilepsy, rheumatic fever or other illnesses?
   ¿Tiene su niño(a) problemas de salud como diabetes, epilepsia, fiebre reumática u otras enfermedades?

4. State law requires the dates and the verification of the following immunizations:
   La ley del estado exige las fechas y verificación de las vacunas siguientes:

diphtheria	**la difteria**
tetanus	**el tétano**
polio	**el polio**
whooping cough	**la tos ferina**
measles	**el sarampión**
German measles	**la rubéola**
mumps (if over 7 years)	**las paperas (si tiene más de 7 años)**

5. State law also requires that we have the signature and/or stamp of the doctor or clinic on the form which lists the immunizations the child received.
   La ley del estado también requiere la firma y/o el sello del médico o la clínica en el impreso que enumera las vacunas que recibió el (la) niño(a).

6. Your child can be sent home if it appears he (she) has a contagious disease or infection.
   Su niño(a) puede ser enviado a casa si se cree que tiene una enfermedad contagiosa o infección.

7. Your child has not been completely immunized and needs to go to the doctor or clinic at once.
   Su niño(a) no ha sido completamente vacunado y necesita ir al médico o a la clínica inmediatamente.

8. Please have the doctor or clinic complete these papers. You must then bring them back to the school office as soon as possible.
Por favor pídale al médico o a la clínica que complete estos impresos. Usted debe devolverlos a la oficina de la escuela lo más pronto posible.

9. Your child cannot begin classes until the vaccination papers are completed and returned to the school.
Su hijo(a) no puede empezar sus clases hasta que los impresos sobre las vacunas sean completados y se devuelvan a la escuela.

10. Your child needs additional immunizations at a later date (in one month, in two months, in six months). You will be sent a notification by mail. You must then take your child to the doctor or clinic, and then bring the vaccination papers to the school for verification.
Su hijo(a) necesita otras inmunizaciones más tarde (en un mes, en dos meses, en seis meses). Usted recibirá una notificación en el correo. Usted debe, entonces, llevar a su hijo(a) al médico o a la clínica y luego traer los impresos sobre las vacunas a la escuela para su verificación.

In Case of Emergency

1. In case of serious illness or accident, if we cannot contact you, what doctor can we call?
En caso de accidente o enfermedad de gravedad, si no podemos comunicarnos con usted, ¿a qué médico podemos llamar?

2. In case of emergency, whom shall we contact? (person/telephone)
En caso de emergencia, ¿a quién debemos llamar? (persona/ teléfono)

3. Is this person a relative (friend, neighbor)?
¿Es un(a) pariente (amigo(a), vecino(a)?

4. Where does this person live?
¿Dónde vive esta persona?

5. You need to find a friend or neighbor to care for your child in case of emergency.
Usted necesita escoger a un amigo o vecino que pueda atender a su niño en caso de emergencia.

6. In case of an actual civil defense alert or natural disaster do you prefer that your child remain at school?
En caso de una alerta de la defensa civil o de un desastre natural ¿prefiere usted que su niño(a) permanezca en la escuela?

7. If not, to whom may we release your child?
Si no ¿a quién debemos entregar su hijo(a)?

8. Where do you work?
¿Dónde trabaja usted?

9. Do you have any health insurance? accident insurance?
¿Tiene seguro de enfermedad? seguro de accidente?

What the Child Needs to Know About Emergencies

- All children need to memorize:
  Todos los niños deben aprenderse de memoria:

their name	**su nombre**
their parent(s)' name(s)	**el nombre de sus padres**
address	**su dirección**
phone number	**su número de teléfono**
emergency number: 911	**el número de emergencia: 911**

- Tape your address, phone number and emergency number on your phone.
  Ponga su dirección, su número de teléfono y el número de emergencia en el teléfono.

- Calling 911

Dial 911 and wait.
Marque el número 911 y espere.

When they answer, describe the emergency.
Cuando contesten, explique el problema.

Tell them your name, address and phone number.
Dígales su nombre, dirección y número de teléfono.

Do not hang up until they tell you to.
No cuelgue hasta que se lo indiquen.

Answer all their questions.
Conteste todas las preguntas que ellos le hagan.

Try to stay calm.
Trate de tener calma.

How to Take Your Child's Temperature

Cómo Tomarle la Temperatura a su Niño(a)

Every household should have a thermometer. One can be purchased inexpensively at any drug store. At the same time, purchase alcohol and cotton balls to keep the thermometer clean.

Es imprescindible tener un termómetro en casa. Se puede comprar en cualquier farmacia por poco dinero. Al mismo tiempo, compre desinfectante en líquido (alcohol) y bolitas de algodón para mantener limpio el termómetro.

1. Clean the thermometer with alcohol and a cotton ball.
   Limpie el termómetro con alcohol y una bolita de algodón.

2. Shake the thermometer with your hand until the mercury (gray line) is down to 96°.
   Agite el termómetro con la mano hasta que el mercurio (línea gris) marque 96°.

3. Put the mercury end (gray ball) of the thermometer under the child's tongue.
   Ponga la parte del termómetro donde está el mercurio (acaba en como una bolita gris) debajo de la lengua del niño.

4. Wait five minutes.
   Espere cinco minutos.

5. Read the number where the gray line ends. 98.6 is normal.
   Lea el número donde esté la línea gris. 98.6 es normal.

6. A fever indicates infection in the body.
   Fiebre indica que hay una infección en el cuerpo.

7. If your child runs a low fever (between 100° - 103°) for several days you should contact your doctor.
   Si su niño(a) tiene una fiebre moderada entre 100° - 103° por varios días, llame al doctor.

8. If your child's fever is 103° or above, contact your doctor immediately.
   Si su niño tiene fiebre de 103° o más, llame al doctor inmediatamente.

9. If your child suddenly develops a high fever (104° or more), you can do the following until you are able to contact a doctor:
   1. Put the child in lukewarm bath water.
   2. Give him or her baby Tylenol.
   3. Give the child liquids and ice chips to suck on.

   Si a su niño(a) le da fiebre de repente (104° o más), puede hacer lo siguiente hasta que pueda ponerse en contacto con el médico:
   1. **Ponga al niño en un baño de agua tibia.**
   2. **Déle Tylenol "para niños".**
   3. **Déle líquidos y también pedacitos de hielo que chupar.**

10. Be sure to contact a doctor immediately. High or prolonged fevers can cause damage to the brain.
    No deje de ponerse en contacto con un médico inmediatamente. Las fiebres prolongadas o altas pueden causar daño al cerebro.

Tips for Good Health

Sugerencias para la Buena Salud

- Allow your child to play outside as much as possible.
  Permita que su niño(a) juegue afuera tanto como sea posible.

- Be sure your child has enough sleep. Many children need ten or eleven hours a night.
  Asegúrese de que el (la) niño(a) duerma lo suficiente. Muchos niños necesitan dormir diez u once horas por noche.

- Some children need a nap during the day.
  Algunos niños necesitan dormir la siesta durante el día.

- Be sure your child wears sufficient clothing to stay warm and dry.
  Asegúrese de que su niño(a) lleve ropa suficiente para estar bien abrigado(a) y seco(a).

- Give your child an opportunity each day to be successful at something and tell him (her) so.
  Déle a su niño(a) una oportunidad cada día para tener éxito en algo y dígale que lo hizo bien.

- Be sure your child has a balanced diet three times a day.
  Asegúrese de que su niño(a) tenga una equilibrada dieta tres veces al día.

- Give your child physical affection on a daily basis. Hugs promote health.
  Déle a su niño(a) afecto físico y cariño cada día. Los abrazos fomentan la salud.

Terminology Lists

The Body and Bodily Functions

El Cuerpo y Funciones del Cuerpo

abdomen	**el abdomen**
Adam's apple	**la nuez de Adán** **la prominencia de la laringe**
adenoids	**las vegetaciones adenoideas**
adrenal gland	**la glándula suprarrenal**
ankle	**el tobillo**
anus	**el ano**
appendix	**el apéndice**
arm	**el brazo**
armpit	**la axila** **el sobaco**
artery	**la arteria**
back	**la espalda**
backbone	**el espinazo** **la columna vertebral**

belly	**la panza** **el vientre**
birthmark	**el lunar**
bladder	**la vejiga**
blood	**la sangre**
blood type	**el grupo sanguíneo**
blood vessel	**el vaso sanguíneo**
body	**el cuerpo**
bone	**el hueso**
bowels	**los intestinos** **las entrañas**
bowel movement	**la evacuación del vientre** **la caca** (child's language)
brain	**el cerebro**
brains	**los sesos**
breasts (female)	**los senos**
buttocks	**las nalgas**
calf	**la pantorrilla**
cervix	**la cerviz**
cheek	**la mejilla**
cheekbone	**el pómulo**
chest	**el pecho** **el tórax**
chin	**la barbilla** **la barba** **el mentón**
collarbone	**la clavícula**
complexion	**la tez** **el cutis**
cornea	**la córnea**
crotch	**la entrepierna**

diaphragm	**el diafragma**
ear (inner)	**el oído (interno)**
ears (outer)	**las orejas**
eardrum	**el tímpano**
earlobe	**el lóbulo de la oreja**
elbow	**el codo**
esophagus	**el esófago**
eye(s)	**el ojo (los ojos)**
eyeball	**el globo del ojo**
eyebrow	**la ceja**
eyelash(es)	**la(s) pestaña(s)**
eyelid(s)	**el párpado** **los párpados**
face	**la cara**
facial skin	**la piel de la cara** **la tez** **el cutis**
feces	**el excremento** **la caca** (child's language)
finger	**el dedo**
fingernail(s)	**la(s) uña(s)**
fingerprint	**la huella digital**
fist	**el puño**
flesh	**la carne**
foot (feet)	**el pie (los pies)**
forearm	**el antebrazo**
forehead	**la frente**
genitals	**los genitales** **los órganos genitales**
gland	**la glándula**
groin	**la ingle**

gums	**las encías**
hair (head)	**el cabello** **el pelo**
(body)	**el vello**
hand	**la mano**
head	**la cabeza**
heart	**el corazón**
heel	**el talón**
hip	**la cadera**
intestine	**el intestino**
intestine, large	**el intestino grueso**
intestine, small	**el intestino delgado**
jaw	**la mandíbula** **la quijada**
joint	**la coyuntura** **la articulación**
kidney	**el riñón**
knee	**la rodilla**
kneecap	**la rótula** **el hueso de la rodilla**
larynx	**la laringe**
leg	**la pierna**
ligament	**el ligamento**
limb	**el miembro** **la extremidad**
lip(s)	**el labio (los labios)**
liver	**el hígado**
lung	**el pulmón**
menstruation	**el menstruo** **la regla** **el período** **la menstruación**
molar	**la muela**

mouth	**la boca**
mucus	**el moco** **la flema**
muscle	**el músculo**
nail	**la uña**
nasal mucus	**la mucosidad**
navel	**el ombligo**
neck	**el cuello**
nerve(s)	**el (los) nervio(s)**
nipple(s)	**la(s) tetilla(s)** **el pezón (los pezones)**
nose	**la nariz**
nostrils	**las ventanas de la(s) nariz (narices)** **la fosa nasal**
organ	**el órgano**
ovary	**el ovario**
palm	**la palma (de la mano)**
pelvis	**la pelvis**
penis	**el pene** **el miembro**
perspiration	**el sudor**
phlegm	**la flema**
pulse	**el pulso**
pus	**el pus**
rectum	**el recto** **el ano**
reflexes	**los reflejos**
reproductive organs	**los órganos reproductivos**
respiration	**la respiración**
rib	**la costilla**

saliva	**la saliva**
salivation	**la salivación**
scalp	**el cuero cabelludo**
shin	**la espinilla**
shinbone	**la tibia**
shoulder	**el hombro**
shoulder blade	**la paleta** **el omóplato**
skin	**la piel**
skull	**el cráneo**
sole (the foot)	**la planta (del pie)**
spine	**el espinazo** **la columna vertebral**
sputum	**el esputo**
sternum	**el hueso del pecho** **el esternón**
stomach	**el estómago** **la barriga**
stool	**el mojón** **el excremento** **la eliminación**
tear(s)	**la (las) lágrima(s)**
temple	**la sien**
tendon	**el tendón**
testicle	**el testículo**
thigh	**el muslo**
thorax	**el tórax**
throat	**la garganta**
thumb	**el pulgar** **el dedo gordo**
thyroid gland	**la glándula tiroides**
tissue	**el tejido**

toe(s)	**el dedo (los dedos) del pie**
toenail	**la uña del dedo del pie**
tongue	**la lengua**
tonsils	**las amígdalas** **las anginas**
tooth (teeth)	**el diente (los dientes)**
trachea	**la tráquea**
urine	**la orina** **el pipí** (child's language)
uterus	**el útero** **la matriz**
vagina	**la vagina**
vein	**la vena**
vertebra	**la vértebra**
vocal cord	**la cuerda vocal**
vomit	**los vómitos**
waist	**la cintura**
weight	**el peso**
womb	**la matriz**
wrist	**la muñeca**

Medical Conditions, Symptoms and Diseases

Condiciones, Síntomas, Enfermedades

(Please refer to the verb list on page 136 for related vocabulary in verb form.)

abdominal pain	**el dolor abdominal** **el dolor del abdomen**
abortion	**el aborto**
abscess	**el absceso**
accident	**el accidente**
ache	**el dolor**
addiction	**la adicción**
affliction	**la aflicción**
AIDS (Acquired Immune Deficiency Syndrome)	**SIDA (Síndrome de Deficiencia de Inmunidad Adquirida)**
ailing	**enfermo(a)** **achacoso(a)**
ailment	**la enfermedad** **el achaque**
allergy	**la alergia**
anemia	**la anemia**
angina pectoris	**la angina de pecho**
ankle, twisted	**el tobillo torcido**
anorexia	**la anorexia**
anxiety	**la ansiedad**
appendicitis	**la apendicitis**
appetite (poor)	**no tener apetito**
arthritis	**la artritis**
asthma	**el asma**
asthmatic	**asmático(a)**
athlete's foot	**el pie de atleta**

backache	**el dolor de espalda**
bacteria	**la bacteria** **el microbio**
bedsore	**la úlcera de decúbito**
bee sting (wasp sting)	**la picadura de abeja (avispa)**
birth defect	**el defecto de nacimiento**
birthmark	**el antojo** **la marca de nacimiento** **la mancha natural en la piel** **el nevo materno** **el lunar**
bite, of an insect	**la mordedura** **la picadura**
bleeding	**que está sangrando** **sangriento** **sangrante** **que sangra**
bleeding, excessive	**la hemorragia excesiva**
blind	**ciego(a)**
blindness	**la ceguera**
blister	**la ampolla**
blood clot	**el coágulo**
blood pressure	**la tensión arterial**
blood pressure, high	**la hipertensión arterial** **la presión alta**
bloody	**sangriento(a)**
bloody nose	**la nariz sangrienta** **la hemorragia nasal**
blow	**el golpe**
boil	**el divieso** **el furúnculo** **el grano enterrado**
bone disease	**la enfermedad de los huesos**
bone(s), broken	**el hueso quebrado (roto)** **los huesos quebrados (rotos)**
bowel control (poor)	**la falta de control de evacuación** **mal control de la evacuación**

bowleg	**la pierna arqueada**
bowlegged	**estevado(a)** **patiestevado(a)** **con las piernas en arco**
breakdown	**el colapso** **la crisis nerviosa**
breath, out of	**sin aliento**
breath, short of	**corto de resuello**
breathing problems	**los problemas al respirar**
bronchitis	**la bronquitis**
bruise	**el moretón** **la contusión** **la magulladura**
bruised	**magullado(a)** **amoratado(a)**
bruises easily	**se magulla fácilmente**
bump	**el golpe**
burn	**la quemadura**
cancer	**el cáncer**
catching	**que se contagia** **contagioso(a)** **que se pega**
cerebral palsy	**la parálisis cerebral**
chicken pox	**la varicela** **la viruela loca**
childbirth	**el parto** **el alumbramiento**
chills	**los escalofríos**
cholera	**la cólera**
chronic illness	**la enfermedad crónica**
clubfoot	**el pie zopo**
clubfooted	**con el pie zopo**

cold (a)	**el catarro** **el resfriado**
colic	**el cólico**
colitis	**la colitis**
color-blind	**ciego(a) para los colores** **la dificultad en distinguir colores** **daltoniano(a)**
color blindness	**el daltonismo**
complications from . . .	**las complicaciones de . . .**
concussion	**la concusión** **la conmoción cerebral**
condition	**la condición**
congenital abnormality	**la anormalidad congénita**
conjunctivitis	**la conjuntivitis**
constipation	**el estreñimiento** **la constipación**
contagious illness	**la enfermedad contagiosa** **la enfermedad que se pega**
convulsion	**la convulsión**
coordination (poor)	**la mala coordinación**
cough (chronic or frequent)	**la tos** **(crónica o frecuente)**
cramp(s)	**el (los) calambre(s)**
cranky	**malhumorado(a)**
croup	**la crup** **el garrotillo**
crying	**llorando**
curvature of the spine	**la escoliosis**
cut	**la cortadura** **el corte**
cyst	**el quiste**
deaf	**sordo(a)**
deaf-mute	**sordomudo(a)**

deafness	**la sordera**
deformity	**la deformidad**
depression	**la depresión**
diabetes	**la diabetes**
diarrhea	**la diarrea**
diet	**la dieta**
diet, healthy	**la dieta saludable**
diet, poor	**la mala dieta**
digestion	**la digestión**
diphtheria	**la difteria**
dirty	**sucio(a)**
disability (physical)	**la invalidez** **la inhabilidad** **la minusvalidez**
disabled	**minusválido(a)**
discharge	**el desecho** **el flujo** **la supuración**
discomfort	**la incomodidad** **el molestar**
dizziness	**el vértigo** **la confusión**
dizzy	**aturdido(a)** **mareado(a)** **confuso(a)**
Down's syndrome	**el síndrome de Down** **la enfermedad de Down**
drooling	**babeando**
drowsy	**soñoliento(a)**
drowsiness	**la soñoliencia** **la somnolencia**
drugged	**drogado(a)**
drugs, under the influence of	**bajo la influencia de drogas**
dysentery	**la disentería** **la diarrea muy fuerte**

dyslexia	**la dislexia**
earache	**el dolor de oído**
ear disease	**la enfermedad de los oídos**
ear infection	**la infección del oído**
eczema	**el eczema**
emphysema	**el enfisema**
epidemic	**la epidemia** (noun) **epidémico** (adjective)
epilepsy	**la epilepsia**
epileptic	**epiléptico(a)**
exercise, lack of	**ejercicio, falta de**
exhaustion	**el agotamiento**
eye disease	**la enfermedad de los ojos**
eye injury	**la herida de los ojos**
eyes, circles under	**las ojeras**
fainting spell	**el desmayo**
fall	**la caída**
fat (describing a condition)	**la gordura**
fatigue	**la fatiga** **el cansancio**
fear	**el miedo** **el temor** **la aprensión**
fearful	**temeroso(a)** **aprensivo(a)** **miedoso(a)**
fever	**la fiebre** **la calentura**
fever, high	**la fiebre alta**
fever, low grade	**la fiebre de grado bajo**
fever blister	**la ampolla en los labios** **la lesión en los labios**

feverish	**febril** **calenturiento(a)**
fidgety	**inquieto(a)** **nervioso(a)** **azogado(a)**
flabby	**flojo(a)** **lacio(a)**
flatulence	**la flatulencia** **la acumulación molesta de los gases estomacales**
flea bites	**las picaduras de pulgas**
fleas	**las pulgas**
flesh wound	**la herida superficial**
flu	**la gripe** **la influenza**
food poisoning	**el envenamiento por comestibles en mal estado**
foreign body	**el cuerpo extraño**
fracture	**la fractura** **la quebradura** **la rotura**
fragile	**frágil**
frail	**débil** **frágil**
fretful	**irritable** **enojadizo(a)** **impaciente** **inquieto(a)** **quejoso(a)**
frightened	**asustado(a)** **atemorizado(a)**
frostbite	**la congelación**
frostbitten	**dañado por la helada** **congelado(a)**
gash	**la cuchillada**
gangrene	**la gangrena**
genital herpes	**los herpes genitales**
glands, enlarged	**las glándulas inflamadas**

glaucoma	**la glaucoma**
gonorrhea	**la gonorrea**
halitosis	**la halitosis**
handicap	**la minusvalía** **el impedimento**
hangover	**la resaca**
harelip	**el labio leporino** **el labio hendido** **el paladar hendido**
hay fever	**la fiebre del heno** **el catarro del heno**
headache	**el dolor de cabeza** **la jaqueca**
head cold	**el catarro** **el resfriado** **el constipado**
head lice	**los piojos**
health	**la salud**
healthy	**sano(a)** **saludable**
hearing impaired	**sordo(a)**
hearing impairment	**el impedimento (defecto) de oído** **el empeoramiento de la audición**
heart attack	**el ataque al corazón** **el ataque cardíaco**
heartburn	**la acedía** **la rescoldera** **el rescoldo**
heart condition/disease	**la enfermedad del corazón**
heart failure	**el fallo del corazón** **el colapso cardíaco**
heart murmur	**el rumor cardíaco**
hemorrhage	**la hemorragia**
hemorrhoids	**las hemorroides**
hepatitis	**la hepatitis**

herpes	**el (o la) herpe**
hiccup	**el hipo**
hives	**las ronchas** **la urticaria**
hoarseness	**la ronquera**
hookworm	**el anquilostoma**
hunger	**el hambre**
hyperactive	**hiperactivo(a)**
hypertension	**la hipertensión**
hypochondriac	**hipocondríaco(a)**
hypoglycemia	**la hipoglucemia**
ill	**enfermo(a)** **malo(a)**
ill health	**la mala salud**
illness, chronic	**la enfermedad crónica**
immune	**inmune**
impetigo	**el impétigo**
incoherent	**incoherente**
incontinence	**la incontinencia**
indigestion	**la indigestión**
infantile paralysis	**la parálisis infantil** **el polio** **la poliomielitis**
infected	**infectado(a)**
infection	**la infección**
infectious	**contagioso(a)** **infeccioso(a)**
inflamed	**inflamado(a)**
inflammation	**la inflamación**
influenza	**la influenza** **la gripe** **la gripa**

ingrown	**enterrado(a)**
ingrown nail	**la uña enterrada** **la uña clavada en la carne** **el uñero**
injury (wound)	**la herida** **la lesión** **el daño**
insanity	**la locura**
insomnia	**el insomnio**
irritation	**la irritación**
itch	**la comezón** **la picazón**
itch (the)	**la sarna**
itchy	**sentir comezón** **sentir picor**
jaundice	**la ictericia** **la piel amarilla**
kidney disease	**la enfermedad de los riñones** **la enfermedad renal**
knot on the head	**el chichón**
laceration	**la laceración**
laryngitis	**la laringitis**
leg, broken	**la pierna quebrada** **la pierna rota**
lesion	**la lesión**
lethargic	**aletargado(a)**
lethargy	**el estupor** **el aletargamiento**
leukemia	**la leucemia**
lice	**los piojos**
limp	**la cojera**
listless	**apático(a)** **indiferente** **lánguido(a)**
lockjaw	**el tétano** **el trismo**

lump	**el chichón** **el bulto** **la protuberancia** **la hinchazón**
malaria	**la malaria** **el paludismo**
malformation	**la malformación**
malignant	**maligno(a)**
malnourished	**desnutrido(a)**
malnutrition	**la desnutrición** **la mala nutrición**
measles	**el sarampión**
measles (German)	**la rubéola**
meningitis	**la meningitis**
menstruation	**la menstruación** **la regla** **el período**
migraine	**la jaqueca** **la migraña**
miscarriage	**el aborto espontáneo** **el malparto**
miserable	**indispuesto(a)**
mole	**el lunar**
mongoloid	**el (la) mongoloide**
mononucleosis	**la mononucleosis**
morning sickness	**las náuseas matutinas**
mosquito bite	**la picadura de zancudo** **la picadura de mosquito**
motion sickness	**el mareo**
multiple sclerosis	**la esclerosis múltiple**
mumps	**las paperas**
muscular dystrophy	**la distrofia muscular**
nail biting	**morderse las uñas**

nausea	**la náusea**
nauseous	**mareado(a)**
nervous	**nervioso(a)**
nervous breakdown	**el colapso nervioso**
neurotic	**neurótico(a)**
nightmare	**la pesadilla**
nits (eggs of lice)	**las liendres (los huevos de los piojos)**
nose (bloody)	**la nariz sangrienta la nariz que sangra**
nosebleed	**la hemorragia nasal el sangrar por la nariz**
nose (runny)	**le moquean las narices le moquea la nariz**
numbness	**el entumecimiento el entorpecimiento la insensibilidad**
obese	**obeso(a)**
ordeal	**la prueba rigurosa la prueba penosa el sufrimiento**
overdose	**la sobredosis la dosis excesiva**
overexertion	**el esfuerzo excesivo**
overexposure	**la sobreexposición**
overweight	**el sobrepeso**
pain	**el dolor**
painful	**doloroso(a)**
pains, growing	**el dolor de crecimiento**
pale	**pálido(a)**
palpitations	**las palpitaciones**
palsy, cerebral	**la parálisis cerebral**

paralysis	**la parálisis**
parasite	**el parásito**
Parkinson's disease	**la enfermedad de Parkinson**
pigmentation, abnormal	**la pigmentación anormal**
piles	**las almorranas**
pimple	**el grano**
pinkeye	**la conjuntivitis**
pinworm	**el gusano** **la lombriz intestinal pequeña**
pneumonia	**la neumonía** **la pulmonía**
poisoning	**el envenenamiento**
poison ivy	**la hiedra venenosa**
polio	**el polio** **la parálisis infantil** **la poliomielitis**
polyp	**el pólipo**
pregnancy	**el embarazo** **la preñez**
pregnant	**embarazada**
prickly heat	**el salpullido causado por el calor** **el sarpullido causado por el calor**
puncture wound	**la puntura** **la herida hecha con cosa punzante**
pus	**el pus** **la postema** **el flujo purulento**
rabies	**la rabia**
rash	**el brote** **el sarpullido** **el salpullido** **la erupción de la piel**
reinfection	**la reinfección**
relapse	**la recaída**
respiratory disease	**la enfermedad respiratoria**
Rh factor	**el factor Rhesus**

rheumatic fever	**la fiebre reumática**
rickets	**la raquitis** **el raquitismo**
ringworm	**la tiña**
roundworm	**la lombriz intestinal**
rubella	**la rubéola**
rupture	**la ruptura** **la rotura** **el rompimiento**
Saint Vitus Dance	**el baile de San Vito**
salmonella	**la salmonela**
scab	**la costra** **la postilla**
scabies	**la sarna** **los granitos que lloran en la piel** (coll.)
scar	**la cicatriz**
scarlet fever	**la escarlatina**
scarring	**dejando cicatrices** **que deja cicatrices**
scoliosis	**la escoliosis**
scratch	**el rasguño** **el arañazo**
seasickness	**el mareo**
seizures	**los ataques** **las convulsiones**
shock	**la postración nerviosa** **el trauma** **el choque**
shortness of breath	**la falta de aire** **la respiración corta** **la dificultad en el respirar**
sick	**enfermo(a)** **malo(a)**
sickly	**enfermizo(a)**
sickness	**la enfermedad** **la dolencia**

sinusitis	**la sinusitis** **los problemas con los senos nasales**
skin disease	**la enfermedad de la piel**
sleeplessness	**el insomnio**
sleepy	**soñoliento(a)**
sliver	**la astilla**
smallpox	**la viruela**
snakebite	**la mordedura de serpiente** **la picadura de serpiente**
sneeze	**el estornudo**
sneezing	**los estornudos** **estornudando**
sniffles	**el ataque de resoplidos** **el ruido de la nariz**
sore (noun)	**la llaga** **la úlcera** **la herida** **la lesión** **la lastimadura**
sore (adjective)	**inflamado(a)** **dolorido(a)** **sensitivo(a)**
sore throat	**el dolor de garganta**
spasm	**el espasmo**
speech impediment	**el impedimento del habla**
spider bite	**la picadura de araña**
splinter	**la astilla**
sprain	**la torcedura** **el desgarro** **el torcimiento**
stamina, lack of	**la falta de resistencia** **la falta del vigor** **la falta de fuerza**
stiff	**rígido(a)** **tieso(a)** **duro(a)**
stiff neck	**el tortícolis**

sting, bee	**la picadura de abeja**
sting, wasp	**la picadura de avispa**
stomach ache	**el dolor de estómago**
stomach cramp(s)	**el (los) calambre(s) del estómago**
strep throat	**la infección estreptococal de la garganta**
stress	**la tensión** **el estrés**
stutterer	**tartamudo(a)**
sty	**el orzuelo**
suicidal	**suicida**
suicide	**el suicidio**
sunburn	**la quemadura del sol**
sunburned	**quemado(a) del sol**
sunstroke	**la insolación**
sweaty	**sudoroso(a)** **cubierto de sudor** **mojado de sudor**
swelling	**la hinchazón**
swollen	**hinchado(a)**
syphilis	**la sífilis**
tantrum(s)	**el (los) berrinche(s)** **las rabietas**
tapeworm	**la lombriz solitaria** **la solitaria**
tearful	**lloroso(a)** **lacrimoso(a)**
tears	**las lágrimas**
teething	**la dentición** **la formación de los dientes**
tender	**dolorido(a)**
tense	**tenso(a)**

tension	**la tensión** **el ansia**
temperature	**la temperatura** **la calentura** **la fiebre**
tetanus	**el tétano**
thin	**flaco(a)** **delgado(a)**
thirsty	**sediento(a)**
thorn wound	**la herida de espina**
throat infection	**la infección de la garganta**
throb	**el latido** **el pulso**
thumb sucker	**que se chupa el dedo**
thyroid trouble	**los problemas con la glándula tiroides**
tic	**el movimiento espasmódico** **la contracción nerviosa** **el tic nervioso**
tingling sensation	**el hormigueo**
tired	**cansado(a)** **fatigado(a)**
tiredness	**el cansancio** **la fatiga**
tonsillitis	**la tonsilitis** **la inflamación de las amígdalas** **la amigdalitis**
toothache	**el dolor de diente** **el dolor de muelas**
touchy (irritable)	**susceptible** **quisquilloso(a)**
trauma	**el trauma**
tuberculosis	**la tuberculosis**
tumor	**el tumor**
typhoid fever	**la tifoidea** **la fiebre tifoidea**
typhus	**el tifus**

ulcer	**la úlcera**
urticaria	**la urticaria**
unconscious	**inconsciente** **sin sentido** **desmayado(a)**
undernourished	**desnutrido(a)**
unhealthy	**enfermizo(a)** **delicado(a)**
unsanitary	**insalubre** **antihigiénico(a)**
urination, burning	**ardor al orinar**
urination, painful	**dolor al orinar**
venereal disease	**la enfermedad venérea**
vertigo	**el vértigo**
virus	**el virus**
vision, poor	**la visión mala**
vomit	**el vómito**
vomiting	**vomitando**
wart	**la verruga**
weak	**débil**
weakness	**la debilidad**
weariness	**el cansancio** **la fatiga**
weary	**cansado(a)** **fatigado(a)**
well	**bien de salud** **sano(a)** **bien** **saludable**
wellness	**el bienestar físico**
welt	**la roncha**
wheeze	**el resuello ruidoso** **la respiración silbante**

whiplash	**la concusión de la espina cervical** **el lastimado del cuello**
whooping cough	**la tos ferina**
worms	**las lombrices intestinales**
worried	**preocupado(a)**
wound	**la herida**
wounded	**herido(a)**
yawn	**el bostezo**
yellow fever	**la fiebre amarilla**

Sex and Reproduction Vocabulary

Vocabulario para el Sexo y la Reproducción

abortion	**el aborto**
birth (difficult)	**el parto (difícil)**
birth control pills	**las pastillas anticonceptivas**
born, to be	**nacer**
breast(s), a woman's	**el (los) seno(s)**
Caesarean section	**la operación cesárea**
cervix	**la cerviz**
condom	**el condón**
contraceptive pills	**las pastillas anticonceptivas**
embryo	**el embrión**
Fallopian tubes	**las trompas de Falopio**
fertile	**fértil**
fertilization	**la fertilización**
fetus	**el feto**
genitals	**los genitales** **los órganos genitales**
homosexual	**el (la) homosexual**
intercourse	**el acto sexual** **la cópula** **el coito**
intercourse, to have	**hacer el acto sexual** **copular**
menstruate, to	**tener la regla** **menstruar** **tener el período**
menstruation	**la menstruación** **la regla** **el período**
miscarriage	**el malparto** **el aborto espontáneo**
nipple	**el pezón**

ovary	**el ovario**
penis	**el pene**
pregnant	**embarazada** **encinta**
premature	**prematuro(a)**
prophylactic	**el condón** **el profiláctico**
reproductive organs	**los órganos reproductivos**
sanitary napkin	**la servilleta higiénica** **el paño** **la compresa higiénica**
semen	**el semen**
sex	**el sexo**
sexual activity	**la actividad sexual**
sperm	**la esperma**
tampon	**el tampón**
testicles	**los testículos**
uterus	**el útero**
vagina	**la vagina**

Prevention, Medical Interventions and Treatment

Prevención, Intervenciones Médicas y Tratamiento

abortion	**el aborto**
aid	**la ayuda** **la asistencia**
analysis	**el análisis**
appendectomy	**la apendectomía**
bath	**el baño**
biopsy	**la biopsia**
birth control	**la limitación de la natalidad** **el control de la natalidad**
blood transfusion	**la transfusión de sangre**
cast	**el yeso** **el molde**
checkup	**el reconocimiento general** **el reconocimiento médico** **el chequeo general**
cleanliness	**la limpieza**
convalescence	**la convalecencia**
CPR (cardiopulmonary resuscitation)	**la resucitación cardiopulmonar**
culture (throat)	**el cultivo (de la garganta)**
cure	**la cura** **la curación**
diagnosis	**la diagnosis**
diet	**la dieta**
donor	**el donante**
dose	**la dosis**
DPT & Booster	**DPT e inyección estimulante**
enema	**el enema**

examination	**el reconocimiento** **el examen médico**
exercise	**el ejercicio**
first aid	**los primeros auxilios** **la primera curación** **la cura de emergencia**
food	**los alimentos** **la comida**
hygiene	**la higiene**
immunization	**la inmunización** **la vacuna**
incision	**la incisión** **la cortadura**
injection	**la inyección**
inoculation	**la inoculación** **la vacuna**
isolation	**el aislamiento**
laboratory tests	**las pruebas del laboratorio**
massage	**el masaje**
medical report	**el informe médico**
medication	**el medicamento** **la medicación** **la medicina**
medicine	**la medicina**
nap	**la siesta**
observation	**la observación**
operation	**la operación**
oxygen	**el oxígeno**
oxygen tent	**la cámara de oxígeno** **la tienda de oxígeno**
painkiller	**el remedio contra el dolor** **el analgésico** **el calmante**
PAP (cancer smear)	**la prueba de PAP para detectar el cáncer**

physical examination	**el examen físico** **el reconocimiento general**
pill(s)	**la(s) píldora(s)** **la(s) pastilla(s)**
polio immunization (in sugar cubes)	**vacuna oral contra el polio** **vacuna del polio** **(en terrones de azúcar)**
precaution	**la precaución**
prescription	**la receta** **la prescripción**
procedure	**el procedimiento**
prognosis	**el pronóstico** **la prognosis**
protection	**la protección**
quarantine	**la cuarentena**
radiation (therapy)	**(la terapia de) radiación**
recreation	**el recreo**
reducing exercises	**los ejercicios físicos para bajar de peso**
rehabilitation	**la rehabilitación** **el restablecimiento**
relaxation	**el relajamiento** **el descanso**
remedy	**el remedio**
rest	**el descanso**
salt water	**el agua salada**
sanitary	**sanitario(a)**
shot	**la inyección**
sitz bath	**el baño de asiento**
sling	**el cabestrillo**
splint	**la tablilla**
stitches	**los puntos de sutura**

surgery	**la cirugía**
suture	**la sutura**
test	**el examen** **el análisis**
therapy (physical)	**la terapia (física)**
traction	**la tracción**
transfusion (blood)	**la transfusión (de sangre)**
treatment	**el tratamiento**
tuberculosis test	**la prueba de tuberculosis**
upper gastrointestinal series (GI)	**la serie gastrointestinal superior**
urinalysis	**el análisis de orina**
vacation	**las vacaciones**
vaccination	**la vacunación** **la inmunización** **la vacuna**
vitamins	**las vitaminas**
Wassermann test	**el examen para detectar la sífilis**
X ray	**la radiografía**
X ray machine	**los rayos X**

Medical Facilities, Personnel* and Clientele

(Servicios Médicos, Personal y Clientela)*

ambulance	**la ambulancia**
bathroom	**el baño** **el cuarto de baño**
bed	**la cama**
blood donor	**el (la) donador(a) de sangre**
clinic	**la clínica** **el consultorio**
(children's)	**(de pediatra)**
clinician	**el (la) médico(a) de la clínica**
county department of health	**el departamento de salubridad del condado**
dentist	**el (la) dentista**
department of public health	**el departamento de salubridad pública**
doctor	**el médico, la médica** **el doctor, la doctora**
doctor, family	**el médico de cabecera** **el médico familiar**
doctor's office	**la oficina del médico** **la consulta del médico**
emergency room	**la sala de emergencia**
examination table	**la mesa de examen**
health center	**el centro de salubridad**
hospital	**el hospital**
hospital (maternity)	**la casa de maternidad** **el hospital de maternidad**
incubator	**la incubadora**
insurance (hospital)	**el seguro (de hospitalización)**
intensive care	**el cuidado intensivo** **la asistencia intensiva** **la vigilancia intensiva**

* See page 128 for a detailed list of medical specialists.

interpreter	**el (la) intérprete**
invalid	**el (la) inválido(a)**
laboratory	**el laboratorio**
lavatory	**el lavatorio** **el retrete**
maternity hospital	**la casa de maternidad** **el hospital de maternidad**
medicare (in the United States)	**el programa de salud nacional** **(en los Estados Unidos)**
nurse(s) (male)	**el enfermero** **los enfermeros**
(female)	**la enfermera** **las enfermeras**
nurse's office	**la oficina de la enfermera**
nurse practitioner	**el enfermero práctico** **la enfermera práctica** **el practicante** **la practicante**
office	**la oficina** **la consulta**
operating room	**el quirófano** **la sala de operaciones**
operating table	**la mesa operatoria** **la mesa de operaciones**
orderly	**el asistente en un hospital** **el ayudante**
outpatient	**el paciente de consulta exterior**
paramedics	**los paramédicos**
patient	**el (la) paciente**
pharmacist	**el (la) farmacéutico(a)**
pharmacy	**la farmacia**
physician	**el (la) médico(a)**
recovery room	**la sala de recuperación**
sink	**el lavabo**
specialist	**el (la) especialista**

surgeon	**el cirujano**
therapist	**el (la) terapeuta**
toilet	**el excusado** **el retrete**
waiting room	**la sala de espera**
ward	**el pabellón del hospital** **la crujía** **la sala**

Medical Specialists

Especialistas Médicos

allergist	**especialista en alergias**
bone specialist	**especialista de huesos** **osteópata**
gynecologist	**ginecólogo(a)**
midwife	**partera**
neurologist	**neurólogo(a)**
nutritionist	**nutricionista**
obstetrician	**obstétrico(a)**
ophthalmologist	**oftalmólogo**
optician	**técnico de óptica**
optometrist	**optometrista**
orthopedic surgeon	**cirujano ortopédico**
orthopedist	**ortopedista**
pediatrician	**pedíatra** **médico de niños**
pharmacist	**farmacéutico(a)**
podiatrist	**podiatra**
psychiatrist	**psiquiatra**
psychologist	**psicólogo(a)**
surgeon	**cirujano**

Equipment, Materials, Supplies and Medications

Equipo, Materiales, Provisiones y Medicamentos

adhesive tape	**el esparadrapo** **la cinta adhesiva** **el tafetán adhesivo**
alcohol	**el alcohol**
anesthesia	**la anestesia** **el anestésico**
antacid	**el antiácido**
antibiotic	**el antibiótico**
antidote	**el antídoto** **el contra veneno** (for a poison)
antihistamine	**el antihistamínico**
antiseptic	**el antiséptico**
application	**la aplicación**
aspirin	**la aspirina**
bandage	**la venda** **la faja**
Band-Aid (trademark)	**la curita** **la tirita**
bathroom	**el cuarto de baño**
bathtub	**la bañera** **el baño** **la tina** (Mex.)
bed	**la cama**
bedding	**la ropa de cama**
bed pan	**la silleta** **el bacín**
bicarbonate of soda	**el bicarbonato de soda**
birth control pill	**la píldora anticonceptiva**

blanket	**la manta** **la frazada** **la cobija**
booster shot	**la inyección secundaria**
boric acid	**el ácido bórico**
bottle (baby)	**el biberón** **el tetero**
brush (hair)	**el cepillo para el pelo**
brush (tooth)	**el cepillo de dientes**
cane	**el bastón**
capsule	**la cápsula**
cast	**el yeso** **el molde**
castor oil	**el aceite de ricino**
catheter	**el catéter** **la sonda**
cod liver oil	**el aceite de hígado de bacalao**
cold pack	**la bolsa de hielo**
comb	**el peine**
commode	**el retrete** **la silleta** **el inodoro**
compress (hot)	**la compresa (caliente)**
contact lenses	**los lentes de contacto**
contraceptive	**el contraceptivo** **el anticonceptivo**
cot	**el catre** **la camita**
cotton	**el algodón**
cotton swabs	**los aplicadores** **los hisopos de algodón**
cough drops	**las pastillas para la tos**
cough syrup	**el jarabe para la tos**

crutches	**las muletas**
deodorant	**el desodorante**
depilatory	**el depilatorio**
diaper(s)	**el pañal** **los pañales**
disinfectant	**el desinfectante**
dosage	**la dosificación**
dose	**la dosis**
dressing	**el vendaje**
drops	**las gotas**
drug	**la medicina** **la droga**
elastic bandage	**la venda elástica**
Epsom salts	**la sal de higuera de Epsom**
eyedropper	**el cuentagotas** **el gotero**
eye drops	**las gotas para los ojos**
eyewash	**el colirio**
first-aid kit	**el botiquín de emergencia** **el equipo de urgencia**
gauze	**la gasa**
gauze bandage	**la venda de gasa**
glass	**el vaso**
glasses (eye)	**los anteojos** **los lentes** **las gafas**
hearing aid	**el aparato del oído** **el audífono**
heater	**el calentador**
heating pad	**el cojín eléctrico** **la almohadilla eléctrica**

hot water bag	**la bolsa de agua caliente**
hot water bottle	**la botella para agua caliente**
hydrogen peroxide	**el agua oxigenada**
hypodermic needle	**la aguja hipodérmica**
ice	**el hielo**
ice bag	**el saquito para hielo** **la bolsa para hielo**
injection	**la inyección**
insulin	**la insulina**
iodine	**el yodo** **la tintura de yodo**
Kleenex tissues (trademark)	**los pañuelos de Kléenex** **los Kléenex**
laxative	**el laxante** **la purga** **el purgante**
liniment	**el linimento**
litter	**la camilla**
lozenge	**la pastilla para la tos**
lotion	**la loción**
medicine	**la medicina**
medicine cabinet	**el armario botiquín**
medicine dropper	**el cuentagotas** **el gotero**
medicine kit	**el botiquín**
Mercurochrome (trademark)	**el mercurocromo**
milk of magnesia	**la leche de magnesia**
mineral oil	**el aceite mineral**
mouthwash	**el enjuague**
needle	**la aguja**
novocaine	**la novocaína**

oil	**el aceite**
ointment	**el ungüento**
oxygen	**el oxígeno**
penicillin	**la penicilina**
peroxide	**el peróxido**
pill	**la píldora**
pillow	**la almohada**
plasma	**la plasma**
polio immunization (in sugar)	**vacuna del polio (en terrones de azúcar)**
powder	**el polvo**
prescription	**la receta** **la prescripción**
prosthesis	**la prótesis** **el miembro artificial**
razor	**la navaja de afeitar**
razor blade	**la hoja de afeitar**
respirator	**el respirador**
safety pin	**el alfiler de seguridad** **el imperdible**
salve	**la pomada** **el ungüento**
sanitary napkin	**la servilleta sanitaria** **la compresa higiénica** **el Kótex** (trademark)
scale (weight)	**la báscula** **la pesa** **la balanza**
scissors	**las tijeras**
sedative	**el sedante** **el calmante**
shampoo	**el champú**
sheet	**la sábana**

shot	**la inyección**
shower	**la ducha** **la regadera**
sickbed	**el lecho del enfermo**
sickroom	**el cuarto del enfermo**
sink	**el lavabo** **el lavamanos**
sitz bath	**el baño de asiento**
sling	**el cabestrillo**
smelling salts	**las sales aromáticas**
soap (germicidal)	**el jabón (germicida)**
splint	**la tablilla**
sponge	**la esponja**
stethoscope	**el estetoscopio**
stomach pump	**la bomba estomacal**
stretcher	**la camilla**
sulfuric acid	**el ácido sulfúrico**
supplement	**el suplemento**
suppository	**el supositorio**
syringe (disposable)	**el jeringa (desechable)**
table (examination)	**la mesa (de examen)**
tablet	**la tableta**
talcum powder	**los polvos de talco** **el talco en polvo**
tampon	**el tampón**
tape, adhesive	**la cinta adhesiva** **el esparadrapo**
teething ring	**el chupador**
thermometer	**el termómetro**
tincture of iodine	**la tintura de yodo**

tissues	**los pañuelos de papel** **los Kléenex** (trademark)
toilet	**el excusado** **el retrete**
toilet paper	**el papel higiénico** **el papel del baño**
tongue depressor	**el pisalengua** **el bajalengua**
toothbrush	**el cepillo de dientes**
toothpaste	**la crema dental** **la pasta dentífrica**
tooth powder	**el polvo dental** **los polvos dentífricos**
tourniquet	**el torniquete**
towel	**la toalla**
traction	**la tracción**
tranquilizer	**el tranquilizante** **el calmante**
tube	**el tubo**
tweezers	**las pinzas**
urinal	**el orinal** **el urinario**
vaccine	**la vacuna**
Vaseline (trademark)	**la Vaselina**
vitamins	**las vitaminas**
walker	**el apoyador para caminar** **el andador**
washbowl	**la palangana**
washcloth	**la toallita** **el paño para lavarse**
water (drinking)	**el agua (potable)**
wheelchair	**la silla de ruedas**

Medical Verb List
(infinitive form)

abort	**abortar**
ache	**doler**
administer	**administrar**
afraid, to be	**tener miedo**
	temer
alleviate	**aliviar**
	mitigar
amputate	**amputar**
anesthetize	**anestesiar**
asleep, to fall	**dormirse**
baby, to	**mimar**
bandage	**vendar**
bathe (oneself)	**bañar(se)**
birth defect, to have a	**tener un defecto de nacimiento**
bite one's nails	**moderse las uñas**
bleed	**sangrar**
blink	**guiñar**
	parpadear
	pestañear
blister	**salir ampollas**
	ampollar(se)
blood, to lose	**perder sangre**
	sangrar
blood pressure, high, to have	**tener la presión alta**
	tener hipertensión arterial
blood pressure, to take	**tomar la presión**
bloody nose, to have	**sangrarle la nariz**
	tener una hemorragia nasal
blow the nose	**sonarse las narices**
	sonarse
born, to be	**nacer**
bother	**molestar**
bowel movement, to have a	**evacuar el vientre**
	hacer caca (child's language)
break	**romper**
breakfast, to have	**desayunar(se)**

breath, to be out of	**estar sin aliento**
breathe in	**aspirar**
	respirar
breathe out	**exhalar**
bruise	**magullar**
	contundir
burn	**quemar(se)**
calm	**calmar**
	tranquilizar
calm down	**calmarse**
	tranquilizarse
care for others	**cuidar a los demás**
	cuidar a los otros
catch (a disease)	**contagiarse de . . .**
	agarrar (coll.)
chew	**masticar**
choke	**atragantarse**
clean	**limpiar(se)**
cold, to be	**tener frío**
cold, to catch a	**resfriarse**
	coger un resfriado (coll.)
cold, to have a	**tener catarro**
collapse	**sufrir un colapso**
complain	**quejar(se)**
confined to bed	**tener que guardar la cama**
contaminate	**contaminar**
convalesce	**convalecer**
	reponerse
cope (with)	**enfrentarse con**
cough	**toser**
cough up	**escupir**
cover	**cubrir**
cry	**llorar**
cure	**curar**
cut	**cortar(se)**

cut teeth	**endentecer**
	echar los dientes
decide	**decidir**
defecate	**defecar**
	eliminar
	hacer caca (child's language)
deodorize	**desodorizar**
diagnose	**diagnosticar**
die	**morir**
diet, to be on a	**estar a dieta**
	ponerse a régimen
digest	**digerir**
disabled, to be	**estar incapacitado(a)**
	estar inhabilitado(a)
	ser minusválido
administer a dose	**administrar una dosis**
drink	**beber**
	tomar (coll.)
drool	**babear**
drugged, to be	**estar drogado(a)**
eat	**comer**
examine	**examinar**
exercise	**hacer ejercicio**
	ejercitarse
exhale	**exhalar**
faint	**desmayar(se)**
	perder el conocimiento
faint, to feel	**estar mareado(a)**
fall	**caer(se)**
fat, to get	**engordar(se)**
fatigued, to become	**fatigar(se)**
	cansar(se)
fear	**tener miedo**
	temer
feed (oneself)	**alimentar(se)**
feel	**sentirse**
fidget	**agitarse**
	ponerse nervioso(a)
fight	**pelear**

fight, to pick a	**meterse con**
forget	**olvidar(se)**
fracture	**fracturar(se)**
	romper
fret	**irritar(se)**
	impacientar(se)
gargle	**hacer gárgaras**
gasp	**luchar por respirar**
go	**ir**
grow	**crecer**
happen (occur)	**ocurrir**
	suceder
	pasar
heal	**sanar**
	curar
health, to be in good health	**estar bien de salud**
health, to be in bad health	**estar mal de salud**
hear	**oír**
hiccups, to have	**tener hipo**
hoarse, to be	**ronquear**
	estar ronco
hospitalize	**hospitalizar**
hungry, to be	**tener hambre**
hungry, to go	**pasar hambre**
hurt (be injured)	**estar lastimado(a)**
	estar herido(a)
hurt (have pain)	**doler**
ill, to feel	**sentirse mal**
ill, to be	**estar enfermo(a)**
	estar mal
immunize	**inmunizar**
	vacunar
infect	**infectar**
	contagiar
inject	**inyectar**
injure	**lastimar**
	hacer daño
	herir
inoculate	**inocular**
intercourse, to have	**copular**
	tener relaciones sexuales

irritate	**irritar**
isolate	**aislar**
itch	**picar**
itchy, to feel	**sentir comezón**
	sentir picor
limp	**cojear**
look ill	**tener mala cara**
menstruate	**menstruar**
	tener la regla (el período)
miscarry	**abortar espontáneamente**
	malparir
move	**mover**
nails, to bite one's nails	**morderse las uñas**
need	**necesitar**
nose, to blow one's nose	**sonarse las narices**
nose, to pick one's nose	**hurgarse las narices**
nosebleed, to have a nosebleed	**echar sangre por la nariz**
numb, to feel numb	**no sentir**
	no tener sensación
nurse (care for the ill)	**cuidar**
	atender
	asistir
nurse (feed a baby)	**dar de mamar**
	amamantar
observe	**observar**
	vigilar
odor, to have body odor	**oler mal**
operate	**operar**
overeat	**comer con exceso**
overweight, to be	**pesar demasiado**
pain, to feel	**sentir dolor**
pain, to be in	**estar con dolor**
	estar dolorido
pant	**resollar**
	jadear
paralyzed, to be	**estar paralizado(a)**
perspire	**sudar**
	transpirar
plaster cast, to put on a	**enyesar**

pregnant, to be	**estar embarazada**
	estar encinta
	estar preñada
prepare	**preparar**
prescribe	**recetar**
prevent	**prevenir**
	evitar
quarantine, to be in	**estar en cuarentena**
	estar aislado
receive	**recibir**
recover	**reponerse**
recover from	**reponerse de**
recuperate	**recuperar**
reduce (weight)	**adelgazar**
relax	**relajar(se)**
	descansar
remove	**quitar(se)**
rest	**descansar**
rinse	**enjuagar(se)**
rub on	**frotar**
	refregar
scar	**dejar una cicatriz**
	marcar con una cicatriz
	marcar con unas cicatrices
scar over	**cicatrizarse**
scratch	**rasguñarse**
	rascar
scrub	**estregar**
	fregar
	restregar
shiver	**tiritar**
	titiritar
	temblar de frío
	estremecerse
sick, to be	**estar enfermo(a)**
	estar mal (malo/a)
sick to one's stomach, to be	**tener náuseas**
sleep, to go to	**dormirse**
sleepy, to be	**tener sueño**
sliver, to have a	**tener una astilla**
smoke	**fumar**

sneeze	**estornudar**
soak	**empapar**
sore, to feel	**sentirse dolorido(a)**
speak	**hablar**
spit	**escupir**
sprain	**torcer**
stay	**permanecer(se)**
	quedar(se)
sterilize	**esterilizar**
sting	**picar**
	aguijonear
strength (to lack)	**tener falta de fuerza**
	estar débil
stress (to be under)	**sufrir tensión**
	tener estrés
stutter	**tartamudear**
	balbucir
suck one's thumb (finger)	**chuparse el dedo**
suffer	**sufrir**
	padecer
suffocate	**sofocar(se)**
suicide, to commit	**suicidarse**
sulk	**enfurruñarse**
	estar de mal humor
supplement	**suplir**
	complementar
swallow	**tragar**
sweat	**sudar**
	transpirar
swell	**hinchar(se)**
take (consume)	**tomar**
take (carry)	**llevar**
take off	**quitar(se)**
talk	**hablar**
	platicar
tantrum, to throw a	**tener una rabieta**
taste	**probar**
tears, to burst into	**romper en llanto**
	romper a llorar

teethe	**endentecer**
	echar los dientes
tell	**decir**
	contar
temperature, to run a	**tener fiebre**
	tener calentura
thin, to get	**enflaquecer**
	adelgazar
thirsty, to be	**tener sed**
throat, to clear the	**aclarar la voz**
	carraspear
throb	**latir**
	pulsar
throw up	**vomitar**
touch	**tocar**
treat	**tratar**
	curar
	atender
	asistir
unbandage	**desvendar**
	quitar el vendaje
uncomfortable, to be	**estar incómodo(a)**
unconscious, to be	**estar sin sentido**
	estar desmayado(a)
urinate	**orinar**
	mear (coll.)
	hacer pipí (child's language)
use	**usar**
used to, to get	**acostumbrarse a . . .**
vaccinate	**vacunar**
	inocular
vomit	**vomitar**
	tener vómitos
wait	**esperar**
wake up (oneself)	**despertar(se)**
walk	**caminar**
wash	**lavar**
wash (oneself)	**lavarse**
	bañarse

watch	**vigilar**
weaken	**debilitar(se)**
wean	**destetar**
wear (clothes)	**usar**
	vestir
	traer puesto
	llevar puesto
weight, to gain	**engordar**
	ponerse mas gordo
weight, to lose	**perder peso**
	adelgazar
whiplash, to have	**estar lastimado del cuello**
worry	**preocupar(se)**
	inquietar(se)
	intranquilizar(se)
wound	**herir**
	lastimar
X ray	**radiografiar**
	sacar una radiografía
yawn	**bostezar**

Schools

Escuelas

preschool	**el pre-kínder** **la guardería infantil**
kindergarten	**el kínder** **el jardín de la infancia** **la escuela de párvulos**
elementary school	**la escuela primaria (elemental)**
middle school	**la escuela intermedia**
junior high school	**la escuela intermedia** **la escuela secundaria**
high school	**la escuela preparatoria** **la escuela secundaria**
community college	**el colegio comunitario** **el colegio universitario**
college	**la universidad**
university	**la universidad**
vocational (trade) school	**la escuela vocacional** **la universidad laboral**
parochial school	**la escuela parroquial**
private school	**el colegio particular** **la escuela particular**
public school	**la escuela pública** **el colegio* público**

* The Spanish word "colegio" is used in some areas for any school, kindergarten through university.

School Facilities

Servicios Escolares

auditorium	**el auditorio**
bathroom	**el cuarto de baño**
bus (school)	**el autobús escolar**
bus stop	**la parada de bús** **la parada de autobús**
cafeteria	**la cafetería**

classroom	**el salón** **la clase** **el aula** **el cuarto**
corridor	**el corredor** **el pasillo**
district office	**la oficina del distrito escolar**
gymnasium	**el gimnasio**
hallway	**el corredor** **el pasillo**
laboratory	**el laboratorio**
library	**la biblioteca**
nurse's office	**la oficina de la enfermera**
office	**la oficina**
playground	**el patio de recreo**
principal's office	**la oficina del director** **(de la directora)**
rest room	**el cuarto de baño**
school	**la escuela**
school bus	**el autobús escolar**
sports field	**el campo de deportes**
vice principal's office	**la oficina del vice-director** **(de la vice-directora)**

School District Personnel

Personal del Distrito Escolar

advisor	**consejero(a)**
advisory committee	**comité asesor**
aide (teacher's)	**ayudante de maestro(a)** **asistente(a) de maestro(a)**
board of directors	**junta directiva**
cafeteria worker	**trabajador(a) de la cafetería** **empleado de la cafetería**
clerk	**empleado de la oficina**
counselor	**consejero(a)**
dean	**decano(a)**
gardener	**jardinero**
guidance specialist	**especialista de asesoría**
interpreter	**intérprete**
nurse, school	**enfermero(a), escolar**
personnel	**personal**
playground supervisor	**supervisor(a) del patio de recreo**
principal	**director(a)**
psychologist	**psicólogo(a)**
reading specialist	**especialista de lectura**
school board	**mesa directiva**
school board member	**miembro de la mesa directiva**
secretary	**secretaria**
specialist	**especialista**
speech therapist	**terapeuta de habla**
substitute teacher	**maestro(a) sustituto(a)**
superintendent	**superintendente**

teacher	**maestro(a)** **profesor(a)** (college or university level) **catedrático(a)** (full professor)
teacher of a "pull out" class	**maestro(a) auxiliar**
vice principal	**vice director(a)**
volunteer	**voluntario(a)**

The Family and Extended Family Members

La Familia y Miembros de Toda la Familia

adopted child	**un niño adoptado**
adoptive parents	**los padres adoptivos**
aunt	**la tía**
baby	**el bebé** (male and female) **el nene (la nena)** **la beba (female) (coll.)**
brother	**el hermano**
child	**el niño, la niña** (anyone's child) **el hijo, la hija** (child of a particular person)
cousin	**el primo** **la prima**
daughter	**la hija**
daughter-in-law	**la nuera**
father	**el papá** (used by children and adults) **el padre** (used by adults)
father-in-law	**el suegro**
foster child	**el niño adoptado temporalmente**
foster parents	**los tutores temporales**
friend(s)	**el amigo, la amiga** **los amigos, las amigas**
godfather	**el padrino**
godmother	**la madrina**
guardian	**el (la) tutor**
granddaughter	**la nieta**
grandfather	**el abuelo** **el abuelito** (term of affection)

grandmother	**la abuela** **la abuelita** (term of affection)
grandson	**el nieto**
husband	**el esposo** **el marido**
mother	**la mamá** (used by children and adults) **la madre** (used by adults)
mother-in-law	**la suegra**
neighbor(s)	**el vecino** **los vecinos**
nephew	**el sobrino**
niece	**la sobrina**
parents	**los padres**
relatives	**los parientes**
sister	**la hermana**
son	**el hijo**
son-in-law	**el yerno**
stepdaughter	**la hijastra**
stepson	**el hijastro**
uncle	**el tío**
wife	**la señora** **la esposa** **la mujer**

Please call 1-800-633-5544

for

- product information
- a catalog
- information regarding discounts

We look forward to

serving you.

Ammie Enterprises
P.O. Box 151
Fallbrook, CA 92088-0151